Psychedelics

Compiled by Thomas Lyttle

Barricade Books Inc.
New York

Published by Barricade Books Inc.
61 Fourth Avenue
New York, NY 10003

Printed in the United States of America

Library of Congress Cataloging-in-Publication Data

Psychedelics / compiled by Thomas Lyttle
    p.   cm.
    ISBN 0-9623032-2-4
    1. Hallucinogenic drugs.   I. Lyttle, Thomas.
    RM324.8.P78   1993
    615'.7882—dc20
                                             93-19655
                                           CIP

First printing March, 1994

Table of Contents

To Linda; my family; my many good friends and collaborators; and of

course to all good trippers everywhere—a high toast to you all!

"Nullah Res Spiritualis Descendit Sine Indumento"

(The Holy Ghost Never Descends Without A Garment)

FOREWORD

By Howard S. Lotsof

For the last seven years I have been President of NDA International, Inc., a medical development corporation which has been established to research and market Ibogaine, a psychoactive alkaloid found in the Tabernanthe iboga plant of West Central Africa for the treatment of chemical dependency, principally stimulants and opiate narcotics.

The serendipitous discovery of Ibogaine's ability to interrupt heroin and cocaine dependency was the result of lay experimentation with a variety of psychoactive substances investigated during the 1960's.

Two decades later, after the original discovery and the expenditure of over a million dollars, NDA International was able to stimulate the interest of pharmacologists specializing in chemical dependency and finally to have the National Institute on Drug Abuse (NIDA) add Ibogaine to its list of substances to be evaluated to treat addictive disorders.

Early in this work I realized we were not only at the cutting edge of science but, in the midst of a medical/philosophical/political battle to determine how hundreds of millions of dollars in research and treatment funds would be spent, how a significant portion of our population using a variety of drugs would be viewed legally and morally by their fellow citizens and the setting of policies which would establish whether medical ethics would be used as a basis to provide health care not only to persons dependent on heroin or cocaine but to the population as a whole. These are all issues that Tom Lyttle attempts to address in this anthology.

I first met Tom Lyttle in Manhattan, at a small gathering arranged by lay ethnopharmacologist and writer Peter Gorman some years ago. At that time I had no familiarity with *Psychedelic Monographs and Essays* (*PM&E*) or Tom but realized Tom's publishing was an important source of information and was very glad to meet him.

A year or so later when the concept of providing Dr. Goutarel's paper on Iboga and Ibogaine (that had originally been conceived for oral presentation at the Museum of Natural History in Paris) was proposed to some journals more well known than *Psychedelic Monographs and Essays* they declined because the piece was not straight science and in one instance "because the paper did not demonstrate that Ibogaine was a drug of abuse."

The importance of the publication of what was to become the Goutarel, Gollnhofer and Sillans' work ("Pharmacodynamics and therapeutic applications of Iboga and Ibogaine," *PM&E*, vol. 6) was that it allowed us to present important information on Ibogaine to the medical and scientific community in a form which could be cited.

I discussed publication with Bob Sisko, founder of the International Coalition for Addict Self Help (ICASH), an addict human rights group that had been running an underground railroad to bring U.S. citizens to The Netherlands where they were treated with Ibogaine by Dutch Addict Self Help Groups in Amsterdam and Rotterdam. NDA International and ICASH eventually reached an agreement whereby NDA International assumed the responsibility to refer ICASH clients to medically authorized treatment with ENDABUSE™, NDA's highly purified form of Ibogaine hydrochloride. Bob Sisko and I grew to have a great deal of respect for each other during this time. Mr. Sisko's immediate response as to whom Dr. Goutarel, Gollnhofer and Sillan's paper should be provided was, "Tom Lyttle and *PM&E*."

We are now hopefully emerging from a period of three decades during which elements within our government attempted to limit information and access to information about the value of psychoactive substances, particularly those which appeared to have the ability to allow the reprogramming of learning and behavior. Such manifestations would be required to effectively treat chemical dependency.

What ten or twenty years ago may have been viewed as science fiction is now occurring as research in neuroscience to study the chemistry and pharmacology of memory and learning as well as the aspects these mechanisms play in our ability to adapt to our ever changing environment. Many of the papers published in *Psychedelics* lend themselves to these new areas of study. Science is about to begin the investigation of the chemistry of psychiatry and possibly more.

Recently the Food and Drug Administration stated publicly that it would permit research in the development of an hallucinogen if that substance showed medical value, provided the studies were reviewed with the same scientific rigor that the FDA uses to evaluate all drug research.

My understanding is that this decision to permit research may have been a direct result of Dr. Rick Strassman's successful work with DMT, the research Dr. Charles Grob proposed for MDMA in the treatment of pain and distress in end stage cancer patients, and the growing interest in studying Ibogaine to treat chemical dependency.

PM&E has allowed information of both scientific and anecdotal research on psychoactive substances to be preserved. This is a course that required both bravery and trepidation. The responsibilities are enormous: The future direction of humanity—war or peace, understanding or hatred, within ourselves and hence, between all peoples.

INTRODUCTION

Rick Doblin
President, Multidisciplinary Association for
Psychedelic Studies (MAPS)

What you hold in your hands is a set of clues to life's perennial mysteries. These clues have been brought to you from the ends of the earth, from jungles and laboratories, from dreams and drugs and Disney movies. From six volumes of *Psychedelic Monographs and Essays (PM&E)*, these clues have been mined. People have suffered to bring you these clues, suffered through intense personal explorations that brought them face to face with their shadows, suffered through intense personal confrontations with a merciless "War on Drugs" that pretends that our shadows will go away in a drug-free world. People have plumbed madness to bring you these clues, looked into the face of death and not turned away, stared at their own culture's self-destructiveness and wept.

What you hold in your hands is a triumph of the human spirit. In the face of repression so complete that psychedelic researchers around the world were locked out of their laboratories for an entire generation, there has still been progress. In the face of criminal penalties so severe that hundreds of thousands of people have been jailed simply for drug possession, the responsible use of psychedelics continues underground. In the face of centuries of genocide, native peoples have managed to survive and sustain their shamanic traditions involving the use of psychoactive plants.

What you hold in your hands is a peace offering, an olive branch and a white dove. The articles in this anthology all have the same subtext, a message of hope that says, "We have information to offer of value to all, drug users and drug warriors alike, if you care to listen." I take this message to be fundamentally different than the message of the 1960's, when counter-cultural opposition to the status quo was felt by some to be a complete and viable solution to the challenges of the day. We are all in this together, as President Clinton so wonderfully reminds us. Those of us interested in psychedelics need to dialogue with those of us frightened by psychedelics about exactly what it is that we find of value in their use. The search for common ground is what this book is about.

What you hold in your hand is Tom Lyttle's contribution to a dialogue of reconciliation. Tom has acted as a bridge for many years between the psychedelic underground, the psychedelic research community, and the interested public. His chosen work has not been easy, for as Timothy Leary said, "If you want to be a bridge, you have to get used to being stepped on." Tom has lived with his share of paranoia, been flung his share of hype and hustle. Nevertheless, Tom has seen his work grow, perhaps beyond his wildest expectations, into an important catalyst of the current resurgence of interest in psychedelic experiences. Tom has chosen to become a traffic cop at a remarkable intersection of interests, trying to impose some coherence and quality control on the flow of information. *PM&E* is read by scientists and underground psychedelic enthusiasts alike, all over the world. Tom's selection of the best of the articles from the previous volumes of *PM&E* make this anthology uniquely valuable, presenting those articles with enduring value in this developing yet ancient field.

I've had the pleasure of knowing Tom when *PM&E* was in its infancy and I was an undergraduate studying psychedelic psychotherapy research. We shared files, swapped stories, tape-recorded oral histories, and mutually supported each other's plans to find a way to focus some of our personal and professional lives on informal and formal psychedelic research. I've been very encouraged to see Tom's work with *PM&E* mushroom the way it has. Similarly, Tom has expressed satisfaction at seeing the growth of the non-profit organization I founded, the Multidisciplinary Association for Psychedelic Studies (MAPS). MAPS is a network of people willing to contribute funds toward government approved psychedelic research. To this network are added foundations, institutions, researchers, drug policy experts and government regulators.

In many ways, Tom and I have been working to channel the same energies. Sadly enough, many of the reports Tom receives contain information gathered illegally outside of government approved studies. Tom seeks to bring to light the knowledge and experience that has been gained by his contributors' self-experiments with psychedelics, or from their observations of the use of psychedelic in other cultures. Similarly, my work with MAPS is to help the scientific community conduct psychedelic research to bring to light the benefits and risks of psychedelics, information already known in large part by people in the psychedelic underground as a result of their personal experiences. Academically, as a Ph.D. candidate in Public Policy at Harvard's Kennedy School of Government focusing on the beneficial uses of Schedule 1 drugs, I work to create policy options for politicians interested in considering how to transform psychedelic usage from an illicit, underground activity into a more socially sanctioned context, designed to maximize benefits and reduce harms.

What you hold in your hands is a part of a larger resurgence of interest in psychedelics around the world. Here in the United States, the FDA is permitting researchers to investigate LSD in the treatment of alcoholism, MDMA in the treatment of pain and distress in end-stage cancer patients, marijuana in the treatment of the HIV-related wasting syndrome (marijuana munchies to the rescue!), and Ibogaine in the treatment of substance abuse. In addition, DMT and psilocybin are being used in basic scientific studies of brain functioning and drug effects. Internationally, several psychiatrists in Switzerland can treat patients with MDMA and LSD. Physicians in Germany have begun to investigate MDE, mescaline and psilocybin. Scientists are going to Brazil to study the use of the plant mixture ayahuasca, to Mexico to study the use of peyote, to Africa to study the use of the Iboga root. Even in Russia, ketamine has been used to treat alcoholics and efforts are being made to secure permission to investigate MDMA in the treatment of alcoholism and neurosis.

What you hold in your hands is the fragile future of the psychedelic renewal of the 1990's. Ultimately, the role that psychedelic play in our lives is going to be judged by our family and friends and the circle of other people with whom we come into contact. The cumulative effects of all these judgements will determine whether our culture values who we are becoming and chooses to find a way to integrate psychedelics, and ourselves, more fully into society. We who are trying to "force the spring," as President Clinton urged in his inaugural address, must do so very carefully, aware that many people would like to put the genie back in the bottle for another generation or two. Be accepting rather than condescending of their fears. Above all, be aware that psychedelics should be approached respectfully, not casually. If you choose to experiment, try to base your decisions and actions on honest, insightful information, like that contained in this anthology. If you are bold and careful, then you, and our society, just might be able to follow the clues you'll find in this book into the heart of the matter. It's in your hands now.

LUDIOMIL, LSD-25 PLUS THE LUCID DREAM

by Joel Bartlett

I am not certain who first introduced me to the idea that I could take control of my dreams by willfully participating in them. Perhaps it was my friend Pete who is an *Eckist* or Andy who is involved in *TM*. Anyway, dreams are a peculiar experience that seem to defy consciousness. Often I know that I had been dreaming but I am still unaware of their content. So it was a pleasant discovery when one night I did manage to bring my hands up into view and I took control of the action in the dream. That was years ago and I have made very little progress if that is what it can be called.

From numerous trips I have learned that there is a special skill that one needs to successfully fathom hell and soar angelic without becoming too alienated from the consensual reality we all call the world. That skill is simply one of diversion. For instance, one night when I was consulting the psychiatric firm of Dr. M. Shrumes I had the most unpleasant internal visions of morbid skulls and rotting flesh bursting from a point. It started to bum me and I could not stop it.

However, I diverted the very real potential for a freak out into a holiday excursion by imagining a narration about personal hygiene sprays delivered in the grand oratorical fashion of the immortal Vincent Price. What was scary became funny and my mute fear became audible giggles. Another example is the occasion I was star gazing through the branches of a birch tree. After awhile the branches stirring in the breeze took on the form of a bubbling fountain of giant spiders...their jointed legs clicking and chirring as they fell about me and scurried away. Enchanted I let this happen for a while. Then, bored with it I conjured up a tank truck shifting gears as it pulled into the driveway. On the side of the tank were emblazoned the word "RAID." A man got out of the cab, wearing yellow neoprene rubber gloves, and said "You the guy who ordered ten thousand gallons of RAID?" He vanished with the spiders as my friend got out of his car, back from the market with his nicotine fix.

I haven't had much opportunity to try such diversions in dreams until recently. I was provided with several tablets of a new tri-cyclic anti-depressant by an acquaintance who had discovered that it potentiates LSD-25. I was cautioned that the only discernible side effect he had experienced was vivid dreams on the following nights. It did indeed potentiate the visual aspect of the psychedelic experience while, oddly, permitting me to retain conventional language facilities. But the real eye opener was the dreams I had on the subsequent night after.

"I was standing on a hill in Antarctica, viewing the lofty snow clad peaks around a bay. The hills beneath the mountains were covered with maple trees and beeches, all in the glorious colours of fall. Well, aside from the erroneous geography the fact that I was dreaming this in full color impressed me for I normally dream in black and white with just one tint of colour, like old water coloured photos of the turn of the century. The geographical errors compounded as I went canoeing on the bay and we stopped (I suddenly had companions) to pick mangoes from the shore. I dropped one into the water and I dove after it. The water was golden and at the bottom was a living room set. I awoke when I surfaced for air (incidently, without the mango)." Laughing, I turn over to fall asleep and hopefully to dream again. Thus began one of the most frightening dreams I ever had.

"I was at my uncle's house for Thanksgiving dinner and it was a bad scene. His house was all wrong with hundreds of rooms and dozens of staircases...holes in the walls and floors to permit spying...etc. My aunt found marijuana in the drawers of one of my cousins and asked me what I thought. I left for a walk to evade answering and found myself in a car with my wife and then walking alone and then in the car...back and forth without any disruption of my monologue to explain the red jacketed horses neatly obeying traffic signals. My roving brought me to a strange neighborhood that reminded me of the French Quarter in Louisiana. Odd for New England. One house in particular fascinated me and I knew that even though I was stoned I had to meet the owner and see the inside of the house. Walking through the atrium I saw walls made of china and wrought iron fences. Two outcroppings of rock emerged side by side, one white quartz and the other purple. I broke off a piece of the purple rock.

"You like my garden?" an old man called out.

"Yes, I'd very much like to see more." I replied. "I am glad of the company. I do not see anyone anymore. Please join me in the garden by the patio," he answered. I walked around to the back and tried to scale a low fence to get directly to the patio where the old man was setting out tea. The fence grew and lifted me from the ground. Below a pool of acid (the corrosive kind in batteries) appeared. I jumped and narrowly missed falling in. We had tea and he talked awhile of his life as an investor of sorts. He mentioned that he had a summer home but that he seldom could leave to visit it.

"Why not?" I asked. He seemed on the verge of answering when he stood up and told me to come inside. Inside I was overwhelmed by the malevolent presence that loomed in the air. The house was full of art treasures...Renoirs on the walls (my favorite Impressionist) and sculptures of every period. But the walls once seen dissolved to reveal new doors and rooms and dark corridors. A heavy breathing began and the old man, frightened, told me that I must leave for my own safety...I now knew why he couldn't leave. I went out into the sunlight and decided that this was only a dream. I must go back and take charge. No haunted house could daunt me I decided so I marched right back in.

"No, no," the old man began, "you mustn't come back in." The room he was in was huge and objects swirled about. I clasped him to my chest and said, "It is you who must leave...this place is evil." I stood apart and shouted at the walls, "I defy you...this is only an illusion, you have no power." I flung one of the rocks I had collected at the mirror. Cruel laughter rose up from the very walls and I stood resolute. "Leave this man in peace," I cried. Clouds rushed in through the windows and the walls vanished to reveal more distant ones. A strong wind pushed me down and furniture caught in the raging eddy battered me. "Stop! Stop!" I screamed. I awoke in a strange bed in the dark...still trapped in the dream. I got up and ran to the stairs which grew longer and longer beneath me. I was still dreaming and with an effort of will forced myself awake. My wife had awakened also, roused by my shouts. I explained the dream as phenomenally good entertainment, however scary.

It was that dream that got me to thinking that I should write an article on the use of that specific anti-depressant as a psychedelic for the dream state. There were, of course, many other dreams, most of them benign and fun. One other nightmare, though, really had me pondering the phenomenon of so called lucid dreams; that is dreams where one consciously participates. It was much briefer and had an identifiable cue in the previous day's activities.

"An ancient city in the jungle. A terrible disease ravaged the populace and they had abandoned it to seek refuge in the mountains. I was part of a party sent to observe and assist in cleansing the populace. This disease was so horrible that it made (dare I use the expression?) leprosy seem like a Sunday school picnic.

In order to infiltrate the diseased victims on the outskirts of town it was necessary for one of us to don the skin of one of the disease's victims. A military operation to begin with made it easy for a general to order someone to wear the skin which we had cut from a dead body. It was gross and got grosser. The 'volunteer' unhappily went into the fungal rot colony, trailed by the rest of us with flame throwers and rifles, and sought to find shelter with the victims. The first one he accosted saw through the disguise and threw up on him. A shot and the flames and she was 'cleansed.' The others fled before us into the jungles. The general ordered the whole of their village razed to the ground and the survivors sought out and exterminated. Amid explosions and bodies convulsing in fire I knew it was a dream and wanted to change it badly so that I wouldn't awake scared witless. I imagined myself to be sitting in a chair watching this horror show on television. It worked, for the images receded to a black and white screen. Sounds came from the kitchen and I reflected that even though the movie was disgusting, I was still hungry." That dream had its origins in a documentary I had seen on T.V. about river blindness in Africa.

For several days I thought about how to write about these

experiences. Then I got a request from *PM&E* to write about "high dreams," dreams in which one is stoned or tripping. Well, the haunted house one certainly had those elements and a little lucid awareness that they were dreams as they were happening. I don't know if they qualify, but they were awesome in their intensity and they did occur before the request.

I suggest that judicious use of LSD and the anti-depressant Ludiomil can have profound effects on the dream state. The skill of diversion, which I had little use for in dreams, was helpful and easier to achieve (albeit with limited success) and the fact that all of these dreams were in living color, when I dream normally in washed out hues of gray with a mere tint of color, have convinced me of their efficacy.

PSYCHEDELICS AND LUCID DREAMING: DOORWAYS IN THE MIND

A. S. Kay

Psychedelics and lucid dreaming are doorways in the mind. Each can lead us to larger realities—often answering a deep need to explore the fundamental question: "What is reality?" Each shows us that reality is bigger, more complex, more varied, and stranger than normal consciousness can fathom.

With psychedelics and ordinary dreams we often jump into uncharted realms. We may well ask: "How can we become adept at exploring these realms?" And how can we travel further?

The answer, as to dreams, is that ordinary dreams are the near shore of immensely exciting Other Worlds, in which we can guide ourselves via lucid dreams, "high" dreams, and high lucid dreams. This article briefly discusses how to reach and experience these higher dream-states.

We know we can train our dream-minds. One clue to this is that Man has learned to navigate other altered states. In particular, there are maps of many means of meditative progress and many phenomena of meditative and psyche-delic realities. And high altered states are increasingly seen to be consistent with each other, however they are reached: via psychedelics, dreams, meditation, spiritual emergence, out of body and near death experiences. So exposure to any of these helps us learn the others. In short, all are comple-mentary techniques for delving deeply into our minds, and all are similar enough to confirm that these Other Worlds are larger realities, not mere hallucination.

Of these modes, dreams and their complements (day-dreams and waking fantasies) are the mind's most universal means of creating and experiencing important higher states of consciousness daily (nightly). In fact, for our mental health we each need to allow our mind to seek its symbolic home by these means, especially by dreaming.

What is the continuum of dreams? Ordinary dreams are known to all. In lucid dreaming you become aware that you are dreaming, and the dream world becomes numinous. If you choose to, you can alter your dream as it unfolds. In high dreams you dream that you take a psychedelic and have trip-like experiences. In high lucid dreams, of course, you combine the "pluses" of lucid dreams and high dreams: you know that you are dreaming, you intentionally dream that you take a psychedelic, and you have a drug free psychedelic trip. Some high and high lucid dreams even continue for a time after waking up. In that state you cannot tell your reality from psychedelia, though you have not actually taken any psychedelic. (These reports complement those from Neuro-Linguistic training that psychedelic states can be induced by micro-modeling.)

Lucid dreaming has been popularized over the past dec-ade, and interest is now burgeoning. Best-known is the work of Dr. Stephen LaBerge, popularized in his book *Lucid Dreaming*. Dr. Jayne Gackenbach publishes the *Lucidity Let-*

ter, and lucid dreaming pioneers hold regular conferences which draw people nationwide.

What dramatic realizations and transformations can occur on all these paths? Aldous Huxley expressed them extremely well as the Pure Light, the intensification of perception (especially color), and a deepening of meaning. The Pure Light has gradations from the absolute, intense light of God down through spiritual realms reported by mystics and Scriptures. The intensification of color and other senses is well-known to psychedelics users, and is far beyond ordinary experience. The deepening of meaning into ineffability is the subjective but totally unshakable experience that each object or image has absolute significance in and of itself, directly, and not merely symbolically.

Another hallmark of heightened consciousness is the suspension of disbelief. The most bizarre circumstances are accepted without question. While in everyday consciousness our minds often generate or receive chains of images that show us deeper connections and laws. Suppose a tree forms itself into a bellowing bullfrog, and the frog becomes a dragon. From higher nature of the tree, or of "treeness," and its relation to the essence of frog and dragon, rather than as a violation of the law that trees stay trees and do not become frogs or dragons.

But these radically enhanced qualities of perception are not important for rapture or fascination alone. Their primary value is in the permanent qualitative changes they can and do make in people's lives. Through such altered states people have healed themselves of physical and emotional trauma ranging from birth trauma to cancer to violent rape. They have boosted their creative awareness, in both art (gaining inspiration and direction for their creative ability) and science (bringing forth new theories and inventions).

In dreams we have complete physical safety. With psychedelics there is safety in most contexts, but since the body is awake and mobile, perceptual shifts can cause danger. Thus in high lucid dreams, with an enhanced perceptual field and only our dream body active, we can safely explore otherwise dangerous or even fatal realms of behavior. This can be accomplished either by taking control of the dream and directing its flow, or by allowing it to unfold and teach us as we remain in a passive student role. Both options are valid and valuable in different contexts, dependent on the dream-tripper's psychological state and the nature of the material that manifests.

Another very useful thing to do in lucid and high lucid dreams is to rehearse our behavior and choices in difficult circumstances, and allow our mind to generate possible results. In this way we can pre-test our waking choices, much as athletes improve their performance by mental practice.

Because the dream and psychedelic states allow us to see underlying patterns that generate and govern our negative behaviors, all lucid dreams also can be used to recognize and release our fears and negativity and to modify our psychological foundations so that we can choose new and more positive behaviors. In fact a good deal of the denial and hysteria that surround psychedelics and "bad dreams" is rooted in the fear of, and the unconscious recognition of the power of, the psychological and psychic aspects of dreaming. But growth usually comes when we face our fears, and we should welcome any path that offers the opportunity for such work and play.

In addition, it has been suggested by spiritual masters that dreams are an excellent place to work out karmic patterns. There we can deal with our deep negative issues without turning them into violence, disease and tragedy in the physical world. For example, such dreams should allow us to work through grief without turning it into cancer. Such ideas have recently received support from experiments that show brainwave activity to be the same for waking and dreaming a given task. This intimates that, to the human consciousness, the two types of experiences are equivalent. While such theories remain somewhat speculative, we are far better off learning to use them as though they are proven, than waiting all our lives for more proof and perhaps passing by the chance to grow and transform.

Another advantage of lucid dreaming is that it is one hundred percent healthy, legal and free. Stan Grof has remarked, after having to turn from psychedelics to holotrophic breathing to help people reach high states of consciousness, that at least they can't outlaw breathing. Well, dreaming can't be outlawed, either.

You can train yourself to recall dreams, do "dreamwork," and then learn higher forms of dreaming. How do you train yourself? By regular practices which I will describe. And if you have had psychedelic experience, that is a great advantage, because it has given you very powerful "track time" in the alternate realities you can reach.

The general technique is to train yourself, progressively, to recall dreams, to do dreamwork, and then to reach successive states of lucidity.

There are dozens of fine books for self-training in dream recall and dreamwork. Any sizeable "New Age" bookstore is likely to have many of them, and all the current ones are listed in *Books in Print* for ordering through most bookstores. My suggestion is that you leaf through several and pick whichever feels right to you. And I suggest that rather than "studying" the book or making learning a chore, you read a chapter, or part of a chapter, each evening just before sleeping. Then invite your mind to give you the type of dream you have just read about. You will find that your unconscious mind is eager to communicate with you, and as you invite dreams and begin your dream log it will begin giving you many more dreams, and richer dreams. The process of learning lucidity will then be a continuation of your early practice.

The same pertains to dreamwork. Don't begin with "heavy" interpretations, like Freudian texts, that may bog you down or may emphasize mental illness or pathology. Instead, start with one of the lighter approaches, like Senoi or Jungian-Senoi dreamwork, which emphasize "speaking the dream" by telling it in the first person present tense ("I am") as though you are, successively, each of several major symbols that appeared in the dream. "I am" is a powerful affirmation in dreamwork, psychology and spirituality. Practice speaking your dreams as "I am"—even "I am" the symbols—and catch yourself when you slip.

Keep a dream log, to record at least the most important dreams of each week. Certainly write down all pre-lucid, lucid and high-lucid experiences to further validate these in your mind.

This initial training process will take most people several weeks to several months, depending on their psychological makeup and motivation. Within several months most neophytes will have at least a first lucid dream, and most lucid dreamers will substantially increase their lucidity.

To regularly reach transcendent levels via dreams, psychedelics, or other tools, however, also requires long-term psychological and spiritual clearing. If we are not clear we give priority to clearing the issues that dog us, whereas if we are clear we find lucidity far easier and more prevalent. But this operates as a two-way street; lucidity can help us dissolve issues. Dreamwork is therapeutic—at no cost.

Many people reach transcendent states at least once in their lives, but to make the level of ultimate unity one's "home" rather than a one-time gift of divine grace requires sustained intention, clearing and practice. This can be gained via meditation, dreamwork and psychedelics, or more easily by a combination of these and other modalities.

Here is a summary of how to learn to have high lucid dreams. It follows the helpful and informative step-by-step instructions in Stephen LaBerge's *Lucid Dreaming*, which he calls the MILD technique. Briefly, the MILD technique consists of two phases: reality testing and dream programming.

Begin as described above, with dream recall, a dream log, and dreamwork, practicing with ordinary dreams as well as any pre-lucid or lucid dreams you may have. This sets your mind to focus more energy and awareness toward lucidity.

Simultaneously begin *reality testing*, by developing the habit of checking several times a day to determine if you are really awake or are dreaming. The idea is that what you steep yourself in during the day is eventually transferred to your dreams at night. If you habituate yourself to asking "How do I know I'm not dreaming?", then sooner or later you will ask this in a dream, and the answer will pop you into lucidity. In fact, if you readily adopt this reality testing, it is likely that you can easily learn and expand lucid dreaming.

In addition to asking this question, you must DO something to check it out. Never answer, "I just know." Among the most commonly used tests are: Jumping up and trying to float. Changing the color of something in the environment. Reading something twice (digital clocks are excellent) and seeing if the text or numbers change radically. Seeing if there is anything odd in the environment, such as floating objects or body changes.

The second part of the MILD technique is to program yourself as you fall asleep by using an affirmation like "As I begin to dream, I will realize I am dreaming" or "If I can see anything at all, I am dreaming." Repeat this as you fall asleep, and again as you re-enter sleep each time you awaken during the night.

Most people have at least one lucid dream within a few months of doing this practice religiously, and many begin lucid dreaming within two to four weeks. People who have had lucid dreams before training often can have two to four lucid dreams some nights after training. The strongest dreamers can train themselves to dream lucidly on command. There is some correlation between normal dream recall and lucid dreams, as to both number and vividness.

Vitamin B6 will greatly increase the frequency and intensity of dreams. It will not necessarily influence the positive or negative content of dreams, however, so you may have both more positive dreams and more nightmares. Nightmares can be especially valuable, though—remember, better in dreams than in waking life. So do dreamwork with them.

What do you do when you reach the Other Worlds? In my own experience, anything you like. I've found it most valuable to do whatever I would do in a waking psychedelic trip to increase my awareness, achieve new insights, reach spiritual realms, heal myself, and increase my psychological integration. Certainly unlimited free travel is instantly available. On the spiritual path, I seek an ally or guide or teacher and may become their initiate. Several people have reported that killing your dream body leads to transcendence and is free from risk. Looking at one's hands is a favorite "Don Juan" exercise that builds spiritual discipline. Accessing the archetypes and becoming them can be a powerful insight and healing tool.

A particularly "psychedelic" way of programming your choice is to decide which dream drug to take in a lucid state. If you take dream-MDMA you will have a heart-level bonding experience, which can be used to clear negative patterns with parents, lovers, or friends, or to enhance awareness of the perfection of your self, and every other person. If you take dream-LSD you can more easily tune into the unconscious realms and the spiritual channels, etc. You might even try creating your own brand of psychedelic, with attributes of your fancy. If you are really daring, take a totally unknown drug, and let it take you where it will. Everything you learn will mirror your mind! You will reach totally new and uncharted lands, which are yet somehow familiar!

Speculative and science fiction stores also offer good ideas for compounding your dream drug. Just so, in *Brave New World* Aldous Huxley introduce Soma, a drug of his invention but named after the early Aryan psychedelic, soma. This was 23 years before he experienced a real psychedelic. Late in his life, in *Island*, he introduced Mokshar as a utopian drug. Time warpers would be drugs that dilate or contract time, or allow time travel to past and future lives. Or take a stripper drug that peels away layer after layer of whatever you see/feel to reveal its deeper essence—then dream a mirror and fall into your core! Or design a transference drug that allows you to be fully in another's mind, or in an alien consciousness. Of course there are all manner of telepathy-enhancing drugs you could conjure, as well as dream tripmates to play with. The list is as endless as your fantasy world, and as deep as your calling.

Here are a few of the high lucid experiences reported by *PM&E* readers, with commentary on their applicability to the spiritual path and the mapping of inner consciousness. They are transcribed in the first person, as each of the three dreamers dreamed.

High Lucid Dream   #1
Healthiness

I am at a health fair where eight different types of psychedelics are being advertised and sold openly at a booth. I decide to try MDMA. Then I *dream* that I remember that I tried this substance last year in a similar dream but had forgotten I had, until now. As I get high, I like MDMA's gentle effects. I definitely notice them as I walk around at the health fair for a few hours. I have a very strange, very mellow feeling, different than with any other psychedelic.

The dreamer had never really had a prior MDMA dream, and had not yet used MDMA in waking life. Shortly after this dream he did try it and found the experience to be very similar. Thus the dream showed his intentions and possibly showed precognitive and/or extra-conscious knowledge. In addition, the psychedelic appears in the context of a health fair, a place where self-improvement is the central purpose. With a little further conscious input the dreamer could then choose to explore healthiness and perhaps self-healing, especially with love. Or he could heal a relationship, by interacting with someone in the dream. These are among the strongest attributes of MDMA.

High Lucid Dream   #2
Transpersonal and Precognitive

I awaken in a dreamscape of small buildings, perhaps out in the countryside. It is a schoolroom and also becomes a boat. I ask for a taste of the "Water of Life," and am led to a barrel-like metal cooler. I sit next to a woman as the boat begins to pull out. In the distance is the Golden Gate Bridge, and I tell the woman, "I am from earth" and ask "What is the name of your world?" She replies "Womb world" or "The Womb Mother."

The "Water of Life" is a very powerful psychedelic drug described in *Dune*, a science fiction novel by Frank Herbert. It has strong mystical powers and permanently transforms the taker into a spiritual leader of the society, if she survives the experience. It is only permitted to women. This dream clearly deals with integration of the feminine on the archetypal level. Both the psychedelic and boat deal with the water element, archetypally representative of the feminine. And of course the alien woman from the Womb World is an even stronger female archetype. The bridge, being golden and numinous, speaks of both transformation and spirituality.

In addition to the normal symbolic dreamwork level, there was a strong precognitive aspect to this dream, as the dreamer was planning to attend a workshop by Stan and Christina Grof on holotrophic breathing, which often precipitates participants into birthing and perinatal experiences. In fact, Christina is a powerful woman whose first two transpersonal experiences occurred during birthing her children. Perhaps the dreamer was turning into the imminent potential of "birthing" into a higher spiritual world. When he attended the actual workshop, he also noticed that a water cooler like the one in his dream was directly outside the building where the workshop was held.

High Dream #3
Spiritual Perception

I partake of the Holy Bread in my old room at my parents' house. Moving through a black and white world, I go down the stairs and step out the front door. Color flashes in. I stand at the steps of the porch and feel the air and hear thunder. Lightning flashes and I am high. Mrs. Miller's house vanishes. I can see the river. The colors are all askew. Sheets of neon green rain under the iridescent navy blue trees, wildly writhing in the storm tossed air.

On the ruby red road the rain collects in pearly puddles and splashes dancing pink droplets. I run in the warm rain, laughing as lightning bursts brilliant purple. I jump into the middle of the road, where four women—my grandmother, aunt, and two cousins—are sitting at a table. I stop to say hello.

At first they look normal, but their eyes have a strange inner light. They grab me. They are possessed. Their faces suddenly transform into horrifying apparitions. Their faces shrink and their hair, mouth, nostrils and ears disappear. Their skin is the color of light rose marble, replete with veins. Their eyes are giant purple raisins.

I become lucid, and know I'm dreaming. I try to twist free and run, but they won't let me go. I say, "I can do all things through the power of Christ." I do a backwards somersault, and awaken.

In this dream, the dreamer takes the psychedelic before becoming lucid, and later his dream becomes a nightmare. When he becomes lucid, (still high) he invokes the spiritual power of Christ to free him from his terror, and he succeeds. The dreamer reports that in waking life his cousins are "born again Christians" and he is Buddhist. A precursor to the religious content is in his initial statement that the dream drug was Holy Bread—a sacrament and a Christian one at that. Even so, he was surprised to find himself using the Christ symbol to reach freedom (and indeed doing a back-flip—a shift in psychological position). Upon waking he saw the dream as helping him integrate the question of good and evil as it arose in his mind across seemingly incompatible religions.

He also affirms that this was the singularly most powerful psychedelic experience he has had in terms of the color negative shift, although no psychedelic had been used in waking life. This indicates that such states can be naturally occurring brain/mind states if we can learn new modalities for accessing them.

Although psychedelics have been widely used for millennia in spiritual contexts, as have lucid dreams, it is only recently that the two areas have come to public attention and popularity in the West on a wide scale. Research into the overlap of these two powerful transformational modalities is in its infancy, and an endlessly fascinating exploration lies ahead.

As more people train themselves to dream lucidly, the foundation for high lucid dreamwork becomes stronger. We hope to build a positive morphogenetic field around the ability to do lucid dreaming, so that more people can easily access this ecstatic state and all the higher states of consciousness it can lead to.

THE 'SEVEN DEADLY SINS' OF MEDIA HYPE CONSIDERED IN LIGHT OF THE MDMA CONTROVERSY

*By Thomas Riedlinger
and
June Riedlinger, Pharm.D.*

Introduction

In 1985, the national news media belatedly discovered MDMA (3,4-methylenedioxymethamphetamine), the controversial psychoactive drug also known as Ecstasy (XTC) and Adam. The U.S. Army had researched this drug in the 1950s, several dozen psychotherapists had been using it with patients since the mid-1970s, and it long had been familiar on the streets among so-called "recreational" users. Yet it seemed to have taken the media by surprise. Thus *Newsweek* (April 15, 1985) was suddenly worried that the U.S. appeared to be "on the verge of either a tremendous breakthrough in consciousness or a lot more kids too strung out to come in from the rain." This breathless statement was a signal, in itself, that the country was actually verging on a different kind of cross- roads: Were we willing to wallow again in the backwash of media hype, such as that which derailed legitimate research on LSD and the other classic psychedelics in the 1960s? Would the public uncritically swallow what it was about to be told by the national news media concerning MDMA?

Yes on both counts. Early news reports from which the public formed its first impression of MDMA were based on press releases issued by the U.S. Drug Enforcement Administra- tion (DEA). Perhaps fearful of being considered soft on drug abuse, the media failed to challenge the negative bias of these press releases. Indeed, many news reports simply repeated the DEA's "party line" almost verbatim. The DEA thus had its way first with the media and later, with conse- quent public support, with the scheduling apparatus by which access to drugs is controlled in the United States. It initially placed MDMA in the highly restrictive Schedule I of the Controlled Substance Act on a one-year "emergency" basis beginning July 1, 1985. (Some of the other drugs in Schedule I are heroin and LSD.) The DEA later requested and got a six-month extension before finally announcing, in November 1986, that the drug's placement in Schedule I would be permanent. It did so even though the DEA's administrative law judge, who presided over three public hearings on the matter and considered other evidence as well, recommended that MDMA should be placed in the less restrictive Schedule III (Young, 1986). An appeals court later voided the DEA's decision, leaving MDMA's legal status problematic.

A full discussion of the arguments advanced by both sides in the controversy will not be attempted here. Suffice it to say that proponents think MDMA has a pronounced, unique ability to help overcome anxieties in guided psychotherapy sessions. They maintain that it facilitates communication between patients who take it and their therapists; that it often has lasting positive effects in interpersonal relationships following such sessions; and that it has no significant history of substantiated bad reactions or prolonged bad side effects at normal dosage levels. Opponents, on the other hand, support the DEA's contention that MDMA has high abuse potential as a popular recreational drug, is not safe and has no currently recognized medical value—criteria by which they claim to justify its placement in Schedule I.

The authors believe that the facts concerning MDMA were often distorted by misleading news reports appearing in national magazines, local newspapers, and on television and radio news broadcasts. These distortions, which influenced public opinion against the drug, clearly involved a phenomenon known as "media hype"—the exaggerated treatment by news media of controversial subjects that the public wants to know about, in order to attract a larger audience or sell more publications. The first author, a journalist, notes that this phenomenon involves what he identifies as seven possible errors of omission or commission by reporters. The second author, a clinical pharmacist who publicly testified in favor of MDMA during the DEA hearings, combines her perspective with his in the following discussion of these "seven deadly sins" of media hype.

The 'Seven Deadly Sins' of Media Hype

1. One-upmanship. Imagine that "we" are a new magazine whose competitor has scooped us on a major story. The competitor's version is published a week before we had intended to publish our own. Since the subject of the story is a hot one, we cannot pretend to ignore it just because we have been beaten to the punch. Our business, however, is news, so our treatment has got to be newsworthy. It must contain new information that was not in the competitor's story, or pursue a different angle, to avoid the appearance that we are a Johnny-come-lately. If there is no significant new information, our choice must be to find a different angle—putting emphasis on something our competitor played down, for example. But what if the competitor's version was not only thorough but balanced as well? Then subsequent, different treatments such as ours are more likely to stray from an accurate basis in fact; the story is distorted. And other competitors, forced to do "better" than our published version in kind, can further escalate the problem.

A report by Emmerman and Van (1985) that was published in the *Chicago Tribune* about three weeks after the DEA scheduling story broke appears to be a case in point. Titled "Cocaine confronts a challenge as yuppiedom's drug of choice," it went further than most other previous news reports in seeking to associate MDMA, the subject of the article, with cocaine, a different kind of drug with an established bad reputation. The linkage turned out to be based on one tentative paragraph within the story, quoting a DEA chemist as saying: "Will MDMA replace cocaine as *the* drug of the late '80s? It's too soon to tell, but it's definitely possible." Except for this attention-grabbing angle, the article basically covered the same ground already explored in other news stories published elsewhere. And later events proved the chemist's concern to be groundless. A 1987 survey of Americans ranging in age from 18 to 44 found that only 2 percent had ever used MDMA or ostensibly similar drugs such as MDA (Methylenedioxyamphetamine), compared with 18 percent who had used cocaine (Sheff, 1988).

2. Sensationalism. Almost everyone is cynically aware that most news media are guilty of this excess on occasion, with some publications and broadcast programs making it a specialty. Sensational-sounding treatments can run pro or con: "Why the thought police banned 'ecstasy'" (Jones, 1986) or "MDMA' 'Madness, not ecstasy'" (Roberts, 1986). It sometimes turns out that the title alone is sensational, but any report that is clearly extreme in its viewpoint or marketed with lurid, screaming headlines should always be approached with healthy skepticism.

3. False objectivity. Many news media, seeking to avoid the charge of being too sensational, are prone to develop a "false objectivity." They might feel a misplaced sense of obligation to devote equal space or time to a discussion of the good and bad effects of a new drugs such as MDMA, even when the good effects outweigh the bad in frequency, strength or significance. This is especially likely to happen when the drug has "recreational" potential that makes it politically controversial, or when the bad effects, though relatively harmless, are sensational or colorful. Thus some reports on MDMA put undue emphasis on certain unpleasant reactions, such as nausea, muscle tightness of the jaw and blurred vision, that sometimes occur as a reaction to most amphetamine analogues. Articles appearing in *Psychology Today*, for example, have consistently dwelled disproportionately on the most extreme cases of MDMA's alleged bad side effects, with minimal discussion of its positive effects at normal therapeutic dosage levels (Shafer, 1985; Roberts, 1986). Readers undoubtedly got the mistaken impression that the ratio of users who have lasting bad effects is very high, perhaps greater than the number of those who have good effects. Yet John Newmeyer, an epidemiologist affiliated with Haight-Ashbury Free Medical Clinic in San Francisco, has observed:

...the consensus of *anecdotal evidence* is that MDMA is generally safe; that is, users rarely seem to suffer any untoward consequences. This means that the traditional indicators of illicit drug use—such as emergency room admissions, overdose deaths, treatment program admissions and arrests—will not reflect much in the way of MDMA's actual usage. (Newmeyer, 1986)

Newmeyer goes on to note that during the first six months of 1985, only 10 of more than 48,000 emergency room episodes reported by the Drug Abuse Warning Network (DAWN) involved a mention of MDMA. This was up only slightly from less than 10 mentions of MDMA in more than 99,000 emergency room episodes during the previous year. Elsewhere (*Life,* 1985), David Smith, director of the Haight-Ashbury Free Medical Clinic, is cited as having reported that "of some 400 drug-related problems the clinic sees a month, only two or three are caused by MDMA. And even then, he says, 'Typically we find the person has actually taken a combination of drugs.'" The symptoms in these cases, including anxiety, rapid pulse and occasional paranoia similar to that found with amphetamine psychosis, "usually fade as the drugs are metabolized" (Smith and Seymour, 1985).

4. Faulty spadework. This problem is usually due to inexperienced or incompetent reporters and occurs when they are gathering background information—doing "spadework." They carelessly fail to find or to recognize relevant facts or lean too heavily on secondary sources. An example of a secondary source would be an earlier-published article by someone else whose information came from primary sources—e.g., from eyewitnesses to an event that is the subject of the article. Quoting from previous articles as secondary sources is not necessarily wrong or misleading, but any such quotes should be clearly attributed. It must also be kept in mind that any original errors in the secondary source will be perpetuated.

Faulty spadework can also involve unreliable primary sources. The problem, in such cases, is when the reporter does not recognize the source as unreliable. He or she might be duped by unqualified "experts" pretending to know more than they actually do about a subject. Or the source might want to knowingly disseminate misleading information ("disinformation") in an effort to influence public opinion. The latter is especially a danger in the case of psychoactive drugs with "recreational" potential. One famous example involved a Pennsylvania state official who reported that several youths had been blinded for life after taking LSD and staring at the sun. The story later proved to be totally false—the official admitted he lied to discourage people from taking LSD (Grinspoon and Bakalar, 1979, p. 172)—but the retraction was not publicized as well as the original report.

An earlier example of how background information can be planted to manipulate the press is even more blatant. Here is how Harry Anslinger, Commissioner of the Federal Bureau of Narcotics (now the DEA) in the late 1930s, paved the way for U.S. Congressional hearings on the Marijuana Tax Act of 1937:

> In a manner that became the model for future drug hearings and laws, Anslinger and company issued press releases describing marijuana as the cause of crime, violence, assassination, insanity and other evils. Newspaper stories headlining the Bureau's press statements were then submitted to Congressional committees as "evidence," supplemented by frightening anecdote in Anslinger's direct testimony stressing mental deterioration, release of inhibitions of an antisocial nature, rape and other lurid tales. Another Treasury Department official began his testimony by stating that "marijuana is being used extensively by high school children in cigarettes with deadly effect," and gave as evidence that of an editorial

from a Washington newspaper supposedly quoting the American Medical Association. A Dr. Woodward, present as legal counsel for the AMA, pointed out that the statement in question was actually one made by Mr. Anslinger which had only been quoted in the AMA journal. (Fort, 1969, pp. 69-70)

For this and Dr. Woodward's other efforts to put Anslinger's distortions in perspective, the Congressional committee "attacked the doctor's character, qualifications, experience and relationship to the AMA, all of which were impeccable" (ibid.). The Marijuana Tax Act went on to easy passage by both houses of the Congress.

5. Careless distortions. Once the spadework is completed, reporters make a judgment as to which of the facts they have gathered are most relevant, which quotes are most representative or interesting, where to place the emphasis in writing up their story or their broadcast script and other such choices. Well-intentioned errors can occur if the reporter is not careful at this point. The best-known examples are taking a quote out of context or interpreting facts too loosely. If a research biochemist says, "I'm testing drug X for toxicity but haven't found the threshold yet," he should not be quoted as saying that the drug has no toxicity. His statement must be qualified by quoting it in its entirety or else by clearly stating that the tests are not completed.

Misplaced emphasis is equally a risk and played a role in distorting the public's perception of MDMA. The media repeatedly have characterized this drug as psychedelic, which, according to some reliable experts, is not strictly true. MDMA's main effect is on emotions—so much so and so uniquely that researcher David Nichols (1986) proposes placing it in a new drug category called "entactogens," from Greek and Latin words meaning "touch within." It does not, in the fashion of classic psychedelics such as LSD, cause powerful sensory amplification or distortions in normative consciousness at therapeutic dosage levels. However, it does have a side effect—moderate sensory amplification—that could be called mildly psychedelic. To conclude from this that MDMA is a psychedelic drug is the equivalent of saying antihistamines are primarily sleeping pills because one of their typical side effects is drowsiness. Yet that is what the media effectively have done in their treatments of MDMA, referring to it casually as "the LSD of the 1980s" (*Newsweek,* 1985) and "the Yuppie psychedelic" (Shafer, 1985).

A more serious common error in reports on MDMA has been to call it a "designer drug" (e.g., *Time*, 1986; *Chicago Sun-times*, 1986). Designer drugs are usually defined as variations on a scheduled drug with psychoactive properties, in which the molecular structure has been altered in order to avoid prosecution under the Controlled Substance Act of 1970 (Beck & Morgan, 1986). According to this definition, MDMA is most certainly not a designer drug, as anyone who bothers to research its background readily can see. It was patented in 1914—almost 75 years ago!—by the Merck pharmaceutical company of Germany.

A final example of careless distortion (assuming no deliberate distortion was intended) is a news report published on page one of the *Chicago Sun-Times* (May 31, 1985) when the DEA initially invoked its emergency powers to schedule MDMA. Headlines " 'Ecstasy' hit with DEA ban," it begins with this statement: "The Drug Enforcement Administration today imposed an emergency ban on a psychedelic drug commonly known as Ecstasy, which research suggests could cause brain damage in its most common users—college-age and professional people." Not until the end of the report—paragraph 11 of 12 paragraphs, appearing on page 28—does the reporter put this startling allegation in perspective by explaining: "MDMA is chemically related to the hallucinogen mescaline.

Another related drug, MDA, has been shown to cause brain damage." This refers to a study, then unpublished, by researchers at the University of Chicago—a study of MDA only. The two drugs are related in terms of molecular structure but seem to have different effects; they are said to be "pharmacologically distinct." Furthermore, the study involved giving massive intravenous injections—many times greater than the normal effective dosage taken orally—to rats, not human beings. Some of the rats were then reportedly found to have sustained what appeared to be damage to some of the nerve receptors in their brains. The DEA felt this was clear enough proof to condemn not only MDA but MDMA as well, even though the researchers explicitly warned: "Given differences in species, dose, frequency and route of administration, as well as differences in the way in which rats and human beings metabolize amphetamines, it would be premature to extrapolate our findings to humans" (Ricaurte et al., 1985). Yet millions of people who read the front-page article in the *Sun-Times*, a major city newspaper, no doubt concluded that MDMA had been proven to be dangerous at normal dosage levels. Furthermore, the article contains no mention of the drug's alleged positive effects until the twelfth and final paragraph, which simply reads: "Proponents of the MDMA, which has become increasingly popular in recent years, particularly on the West Coast, say it has the ability to make people trust each other and to break down barriers."

6. Deliberate distortions. Distorted presentations of a subject in the news are not always due to carelessness. Reporters, editors and radio and television news directors sometimes express a strong personal bias by consciously distorting certain facts in preparing their news stories. Three examples of the methods used to forge these malicious distortions are trivialization, selective quote polishing and selective representation. The first two should be obvious to readers or viewers who know what to watch for. The third is more insidious.

Trivialization involves placing information in the context of a sentence that is phrased to make the subject sound irrelevant or silly. The following lines from an article on MDMA that was published in *Omni* magazine are a case in point: "One dealer gives written 'flight instructions' promising that while XTC is 'kissing in your veins' during the hour-long voyage, you'll experience happiness, security, peace, and freedom. That should end all wars, but secret U.S. Army tests in the Fifties found that it ended the lives of experimental animals" (Siegel, 1985). The writer of this passage did not bother to explain that every drug, even aspirin, has a toxic level at which death occurs when too much is injected or ingested. Toxicity tests on animals often involve injecting or feeding them progressively higher doses of a substance until death occurs, thus pegging the precise lethal dosage. By ignoring this fact, the writer of the article appeared to be hinting that MDMA is potentially fatal within normal therapeutic dosage levels, which is not the case at all. A few months earlier, the *Brain/Mind Bulletin* (1985) had reported, after noting that MDMA had been taken an estimated one million times since the 1970s, that only one overdose death with complications had been traced to the sole use of MDMA, and that in four post-mortems MDMA had been found to be one of a combination of drugs.

Selective quote polishing illustrates a journalistic axiom: If you want to make someone sound foolish, try quoting him or her verbatim. Most people think that they want to be quoted verbatim, but in fact it is more common—and charitable—for journalists to "polish" quotations for clarification. A negative example of the reason this is done involved George Bush, the U.S. vice president during the Reagan administration. While campaigning in 1988 for the presidential nomination of the Republican party, Bush was asked: "Why do so many Americans want to use drugs? Is there some underlying cause in American life?" Roger Simon, a newspaper columnist, reported Bush's answer almost word-for-word:

"Yeah, I think there's some social change going on...AIDS, for example, uh, is a, is a, uh, disease for, disease of poverty, in a sense. It's where the hopelessness is. It's bigger than that, of course...(and) the hopelessness that comes when you have AIDS interjecting with narcotics, all of which stems from some kind of a cycle of hopelessness in some areas, not across the whole country. The whole country is doing pretty well in a lot of ways. More Americans at work than any time in the history of this country and a higher percentage of the work force, but I don't think there's quote a malaise unquote in this country. I think there are some serious problems out there, that your question is a very deep and philosophical one. And of course there are current sociological currents in this country that, that uh, lead people to conduct their lives in some ways, but I am one who thinks that at various times in our history we have condoned some of the things we should have condemned. We have gotten away from values in school, for one. Some of it is out of this post-Watergate, post-Vietnam syndrome, where our kids were taught, for example, about Vietnam, that we were all immoral. My kids were taught that by good, smart people, who agonized over the war, and look at Vietnam today. We go through cycles, it seems to me. So, yes, there's some underpinnings of discontent, but I don't think that should be an excuse for tolerating the use of narcotics." (Simon, 1988)

Another reporter might have given Bush the chance to try again and make his statement more concisely, or could have paraphrased his comments. But journalists who want to put the person being quoted in a bad light are more likely to quote the original comment verbatim. Attentive listeners or readers will notice, in such cases, that the people being quoted on one side of an issue sound consistently less eloquent than those on the side that is favored by the journalist.

Selective representation has a similar goal. Arthur Kleps, in *Millbrook: The True Story of the Early Years of the Psychedelic Revolution,* gives a good explanation of how and why this tactic is employed:

> [In the mid-1960s], the voices of psychedelic advocates were getting a public hearing even though the laws were against us. Since then, the government and the establishment press have learned to avoid such open disputation and space and time are granted only to those anti-establishment figures most likely to offend the general public while all others are quietly ignored. It is the best tactic, certainly. The appearance of an open dialogue is maintained, but one's collective opponent is caricatured by control over his lineup.... It is more insidious and destructive than outright suppression, because it is so difficult to recognize for what it is. As far as the average man is concerned, our side has been getting, if anything, more than a fair share of media space and time. (Kleps, 1977, pp. 112-113)

7. The Frankenstein effect. In Mary Shelley's novel *Frankenstein*, a man creates and then loses control of a monster whose subsequent behavior is increasingly sociopathic. Similarly, journalists sometimes make runaway media monsters of the controversial subjects they sensationalize.

Symptomatic of this "Frankenstein effect" would be the bad reaction stories that inevitably follow in the wake of a successful hype concerning psychoactive drugs. Such hype, whether pro or con, is almost certain to fuel a demand for the product much greater than what had existed before the hype started. Furthermore, the speed with which the story is developed and exploited by the media ensures that such demand will likely grow within a relatively short amount of time. Clandestine laboratories, cranking up to generate the quantities required to cash in on this demand, might be tempted to cut corners to get out the product as quickly as possible. Quality then suffers; the clandestine labs start using inferior chemical components, mixing batches insufficiently and thus producing dosages of uneven strength, and so forth. Dealers, too, are pressured by burgeoning orders for the drug that is effectively being promoted by media hype. If dealers do not have the hot new drug in stock, they will sometimes offer something else they feel can be passed off as the product that their customers are asking for. The end result can be a surge of "bad trip" stories that the media attribute to the drug itself, without pointing out that the dosages causing the problem are possibly adulterated.

Inexperienced users contribute additional bad trip stories. In describing what he calls "a natural history of the assimilation of an intoxicating drug by a society," Becker observes:

> The ability of the drug to alter subjective experience in desirable ways becomes known to increasing numbers of people, and the drug itself simultaneously becomes available, along with the information needed to make its use effective. Use increases, but users do not have a sufficient amount of experience with the drug to form a stable conception of it...They do not know what it can do to the mind, have no firm idea of the variety of effects it can produce, and are not sure how permanent or dangerous the effects are. They do not know if the effects can be controlled or how. No drug-using culture exists, and there is thus no authoritative alternative with which to counter the possible definition, when and if it comes to mind, of the drug experience as madness. "Psychotic episodes" occur frequently. (Becker, 1967)

The lack of what he calls an "authoritative alternative" affects not only users but the media as well, Becker argues:

Journalists use any number of approaches conventional in their craft; what they write is greatly influenced by their own professional needs. They must write about "news," about events which have occurred recently and require reporting and interpretation. Furthermore, they need "sources," persons to whom authoritative statements can be attributed. Both needs dispose them to reproduce the line taken by law enforcement officials and physicians, for news is often made by the passage of a law or by a public statement in the wake of an alarming event, such as a bizarre murder or suicide. So journalistic reports frequently dwell on the theme of madness or suicide, a tendency intensified by the newsman's desire to tell a dramatic story. (ibid.)

Eventually, Becker continues, those who use the new drug accumulate experience and share what they have learned with others. A consensus develops about the drug's effects, proper dosage, and how to avoid its predictable dangers. "Psychotic episodes' occur less frequently in proportion to the growth of the [drug] culture to cover the range of possible effects and its spread to a greater proportion of users," he concludes. Until this occurs, however, all bad trips will be taken as grist for the media's mill and widely publicized. The drug's opponents then will claim that their earlier warnings are vindicated.

Conclusion

LSD and the other suppressed psychedelics may yet overcome their initial bad press. But the new generation of mind drugs represented by MDMA hold too much demonstrated promise for dramatically improving mental health to allow them to languish in similar fashion for so many years. Journalists and health care professionals alike must take a vested interest in critically evaluating stories on the benefits and dangers of these drugs, and we should be much less forgiving when we recognize factual errors, distortions and oversights. The gravity of this responsibility cannot be stated better than these lines from Herman Hesse:

> It is treason to sacrifice love of truth, intellectual honesty, loyalty to the laws and methods of the mind, to any other interests, including those of one's country. Whenever propaganda and the conflict of interests threatens to devalue, distort, and do violence to the truth...it is our duty to resist and save the truth, or rather the striving for truth, since that is the supreme article of our creed. The scholar who knowingly speaks, writes, or teaches falsehood, who knowingly supports lies and deceptions, not only violates organic principles. He also, no matter how things may seem at the given moment, does his people a grave disservice. (Hesse, 1970, p. 332)

References

Beck, J., and Morgan, P.A. "Designer drug confusion: a focus on MDMA." *Journal of Drug Education* 1986; 16 (3):267-282.

Becker, H.S. "History, culture and subjective experience: an exploration of the social bases of drug-induced experiences." *Journal of Health and Social Behavior* 1986;8(9): 163-176.

Brain/Mind Bulletin. "MDMA: compound raises medical, legal issues." April 15, 1985:1-2.

Chicago Sun-Times. " 'Ecstasy' hit with DEA ban." May 31, 1985:1,28.

Chicago Sun-Times. "New 'designer drugs' deadlier than heroin." November 21, 1986:7.

Emmerman, L., and Van, J. "Cocaine confronts a challenge as yuppiedom's drug of choice." *Chicago Tribune* July 25, 1985; section 2:1-2.

Fort, J. *The Pleasure Seekers: The Drug Crisis, Youth and Society.* Bobbs-Merrill: New York, 1969.

Grinspoon, L, and Bakalar, J.B., *Psychedelic Drugs Reconsidered.* Basic Books: New York, 1979.

Hesse, H. *Magister Ludi (The Glass Bead Game).* Bantam Books: New York, 1970

Jones, R. "Why the thought police banned ecstasy." *Simply Living* 1986;2(10):91-95.

Kleps, A. *Millbrook: The True Story of the Early Years of the Psychedelic Revolution.* Bench Press: Oakland, California, 1977.

Life. "The trouble with ecstasy." August 1985;8(9):88-94.

Newmeyer, J.A. "Some considerations on the prevalence of MDMA use." *Journal of Psychoactive Drugs* 1986;18(4):361-362.

Newsweek. "Getting high on 'ecstasy.'" April 15, 1985:96.

Nichols, D.E. "Differences between the mechanism of action of MDMA, MBDB, and the classic hallucinogens. Identification of a new therapeutic class: entactogens." *Journal of Psychoactive Drugs* 1986; 18(4):305-313.

Ricaurte, G., Bryan, G., Strauss, L., Seiden, L., and Schuster, C. "Hallucinogenic amphetamine selectively destroys brain serotonin nerve terminals." *Science* September 6, 1985:229: 986-988.

Roberts, M. "MDMA: 'Madness, not ecstasy.'" *Psychology Today* June 1986:14-15.

Shafer, J. "MDMA: psychedelic drug faces regulation." *Psychology Today* May 1985:68-69.

Sheff, D. "Sex, drugs and rock & roll." *Rolling Stone* May 5, 1988:57-58,65.

Siegel, R.K. "Chemical ecstasies." *Omni* August 1985:29.

Simon, R. "If it's awesome, let George Do it." *Chicago Tribune* April 22, 1988; section 2:1.

Smith, D.E., and Seymour, R.B., "Clarification of 'designer' drugs." *The U.S. Journal* November 1985:9.

Time. "The next high." September 15, 1986:68.

Young, F.L. "Opinion and recommended ruling, findings of fact, conclusions of law and decision of administrative law judge." Submitted in the matter of MDMA scheduling, docket no. 84-48. United States Department of Justice. Drug Enforcement Administration. May 22, 1986.

THE BREACHING OF DON JUAN'S TEACHING: A TWENTY YEAR REVIEW OF CARLOS CASTANEDA'S *THE TEACHING OF DON JUAN: A YAQUI WAY OF KNOWLEDGE* (1968)

by Ray Clare

The Breaching of Don Juan's Teaching

In June 1967 the Beatles released their eighth album, titled *Sergeant Pepper's Lonely Hearts Club Band.* The musicians, disguised in beards, moustaches and long hair, were portrayed on the front cover of the album donned in dazzling colorful satin paramilitary uniforms. Surrounded by an entourage of well-known celebrities, the disguised musicians appeared to project the roles of marching bandleaders, magicians, and

circus ringmasters. Lyrics to the songs on the novel psychedelic album were printed for the first time on the back jacket
of the album cover, beckoning fans to join them in the
media-projected pageant in the spirit of participation mystique. The songs themselves were superimposed tracks of
studio-recorded music. Syncretizing various popular music
streams, the recordings evoked the sensory phenomena of
synesthesia characteristics of the psychedelic drug experience.

Reviewing the landmark album of the mixed-media saturated Sixties in 1987, British music critic William Mann
commented in the BBC television special "It was Twenty
Years Ago Today" that when you hear the album again today
it still conjures up that period now gone. "That's what music
is about," Mann noted, "to encapsulate the period in which it
was written."

As the Beatles' masterpiece album *Sergeant Pepper's Lonely
Hearts Club Band* encapsulated the expanded consciousness
of 1967 in music, Carlos Castaneda's underground best-seller
The Teachings of Don Juan encapsulated the liminal consciousness of students coming of age in the Psychedelic
Sixties in literature. Like the fate of *Sergeant Pepper's Lonely
Hearts Club Band* heralded in the lyrics to the album's title
song track, sorcerer apprentices were destined to come in
and go out of style, but the apprentice allegorized by Castaneda
in the classic campus cult book of the '60s was guaranteed to
conjure a smile. So may I introduce you the anthropologist
we've known for all these years....

In 1967 UCLA graduate anthropology student Carlos Castaneda
presented a copy of his manuscript *The Teachings of Don
Juan* to a professor for comments. Impressed by the graduate student's literary work, the UCLA anthropologist and
ethnomethodologist professor encouraged Castaneda to show
his manuscript to the University of California Press (de Mille,
1980:84). In late 1967, three editors of the Press read the

manuscript and concurred it was quite novel. Four anthropologists from the University of California at Los Angeles
campus studied the manuscript and recommended the
Mesoamerican ethnography work for publication.

One UCLA faculty member not consulted by the University
of California Press to review Carlos Castaneda's manuscript in
1967 was anthropology professor Ralph Beals, a Yaqui Indian
specialist. Eleven years later at an anthropology symposium,
Beals would publicly criticize the editors of the Press for
neglecting to consult him and Yaqui specialist Edward Spicer for an opinion on Castaneda's manuscript (de Mille,
1980:123,134). The editors of the Press didn't consult Yaqui
specialists Ralph Beals and Edward Spicer in 1967 probably
because they didn't believe it was necessary. Castaneda only
mentioned the term "Yaqui" once in the text, when he
introduced his anonymous teacher don Juan as a Yaqui
Indian. Castaneda's anthropology work slipped by the critical
scrutiny of manuscript reviewers, between the worlds of
Yaqui ethnography specialists in 1967, because the author
displaced and played down the Yaqui cultural context of don
Juan in his text. Had Castaneda definitively described don
Juan's Yaqui cultural milieu in *The Teachings,* UC Press
editors would have been prompted to consult Yaqui cultural
anthropologists Ralph Beals and Edward Spicer to get their
expert opinions on the manuscript.

Castaneda disguised don Juan's anomalous Yaqui cultural
role so effectively no cultural anthropologist ever detected it,
although it was their professional job to identify it. Cognizant
of the anomalous cultural milieu of don Juan, Castaneda
stated at the outset of the book that he had no intention of
identifying it. It appears that Castaneda wrote *The Teachings
of Don Juan* so that it would not be scrutinized and shot
down by Yaqui ethnography manuscript reviewers. *The Teachings of Don Juan* was an ethnography riddle and an

ethnomethodological "breaching" test for advanced anthropology students (de Mille, 1980:69-72, 81-84). Ethnoscientific
classification of the allegorized reality of *The Teachings* was
no task for novice anthropology students. Most professional
anthropologists left the ethnography riddle unresolved and
dismissed the book in the '70s as a hoax. Castaneda's leading
critic, writer Richard de Mille, derisively stated in his 1980
exhaustive book *The Don Juan Papers* that the riddle of the
don Juan allegory could be left to hippies.

The ethnomethodology test for anthropology students to
pass in *The Teachings* was to "see" a native reality between
the world of the sorcerer's apprentice and the sorcerer. The
final lesson for readers to learn from the text was how to
enter the crack between worlds. This disclosure at the end of
the book was a clue to understanding the approach to the
book's cryptic allegory. Carlos' incomplete apprenticeship in
the sorcerer's world culminated in another passage rite
initiation test. The fictitious Yaqui sorcerer's apprenticeship
reported in the narrative was subsumed at the end of the
book by a Pascola world "breaching" test. Pascola is the
hispanicized folk name of the bearded, masked Yaqui clown.
I propose the term means "old masked man." The uninitiated
reader who failed to enter the crack between the worlds
described in the narrative remained "betwixt and between,"
in a state of liminality, deceived by the sorcerer's world and
unconscious of the second more comprehensive apprenticeship
allegorized in the book; a Yaqui Pascola apprenticeship. The
particular task for anthropologists to learn was how to enter
the Pascola world in Castaneda's book.

Castaneda explained in his second and third books that a
"man of knowledge" was a sorcerer who understood another
interpretation that allowed for an alternative cognitive structure, i.e., a "separate reality." Castaneda reported this mode
of interpretation was called "seeing." "Seeing" only happened

when a man sneaked between the worlds of living men and sorcerers. One year before Carlos met don Juan in an Arizona bordertown in 1960, graduate anthropology student Vera Laski briefly described Pueblo Indian clowns in New Mexico as seers and masters of ceremony (1959:13). Clowns themselves are invisible, and since they can see what no one else can perceive, i.e., the invisible, they "see" and announce the masked personae of public rites. Ethnomethodology student Carlos Castaneda got inside the native head of Yaqui clowns in the '60s and sneaked between worlds invisible to Yaqui cultural anthropologists. Anthropologists who dismissed don Carlos' reported apprenticeship in *The Teachings* as a hoax were not aware of the ethnography loophole that Castaneda found and exploited in Yaqui Pascola oral literature. Anthropologist and non-anthropologist Edward Spicer's Pascola-blind book review published in April 1969, (Noel, 1976: 29-33). Ralph Beals, the UCLA anthropologist who discovered Yaqui Pascola clowns in 1931. never understood the don Juan allegory. Beals first introduced Yaqui clowns to American anthropologists in 1934, noting that the Yaquis of Sonora referred to the clowns as Diablos (devils). Castaneda's 1968 book opened with a discussion of sorcerers the Sonoran Indians identified as diableros (devils).

The elusive anthropologist called his 1971 sequel *A Separate Reality*. The crux of *The Teachings* was not to uncover a Piltdown-level hoax and expose a trickster, as Richard de Mille did in 1976 and 1980, but to unmask a Yaqui clown as a passage rite specialist and understand a "separate reality" that allowed for a sensible explanation of the fictitious anomalous events reported in the book. The separate reality of the Pascola is the proper milieu against which to evaluate Castaneda's apprenticeship in Yaqui culture. Previous anthropologists separated the way of the modern Pascola from shamanism. Ralph Beals suggested though the ancient Yaqui

Pascola may have had a shamanistic character (1943:70). The path of the Pascola in Yaqui culture is individually stylized, esoteric and traditionally acquired through apprenticeship. The crux of ethnomethodology is to enter another reality and gain membership. Anthropology students were supposed to acquire membership of a Yaqui "separate reality" that subsumed Carlos' fictitious narrative through the phenomenology method. Had Castaneda's manuscript reviewers breached the "separate reality" of a Pascola allegorized in *The Teachings of Don Juan* in 1967, they would never have published it as a scientific anthropology book on Yaqui sorcery.

The word "Yaqui" in the book's subtitle did not appear in the original manuscript read by reviewers. After Castaneda's manuscript was accepted for publication, the UC Press editorial committee suggested the term "Yaqui" be added to the title *The Teachings of Don Juan* to identify the book ethnographically. The University of California Press credited Castaneda with the authorship of the title and the subtitle of the dual apprenticeship book. Carlos Castaneda's first book *The Teachings of Don Juan: A Yaqui Way of Knowledge* was publically released by the University of California Press twenty years ago on June 27, 1968.

Seduced by the contemporary transpersonal psychology subjects of hallucinogens, shamanism and altered states of consciousness dealt with at length in the book, thousands of drug-curious students in the late '60s engrossed themselves in the don Juan mystique. Five years after the campus cult book's first printing, the second printing of the underground best-seller sold 16,000 prints a week.

In the early 1970s, some book review critics, such as anthropologist Vincent Crapanzano, briefly commented upon the phenomenon of clowning that pervaded Castaneda's books. Crapanzano recounted in 1973 that don Genaro's clowning eventually disoriented Carlos to the point where the anthropology student was at the threshold of seeing. Book review critics noted that Castaneda's characters behaved in the role of a clown, like those observed in other cultures. These reviewers classified the ethnomethodologist author's characters ethically, in terms of universal phenomenal distinctions. They neglected to ethnoscientifically classify the writer's characters emically; i.e., in terms of cultural-specific phenomenal distinctions. Leading book review critics failed to phenomenologically penetrate the enchanted goat-masked world of the Yaqui clown allegorized in *The Teachings of Don Juan*. Castaneda's characters behaved in a cultural-specific manner: a Yaqui way.

A Yaqui Way of Pascola Behavior

1. Misuse titles of persons; miscall members of the audience by wrong kinship titles.
2. Deliberately misuse words, ideas, play on words.
3. Induct members of the audience into their world; carry on nonserious absurd conversations; discuss social contexts of imaginary persons; focus on conflicting attitudes; comment on town controversies and activities and twist them into odd forms; maintain a constant exchange with the audience; effectively draw oral responses from the male audience; elicit comment from articulate persons in the audience.
4. Jointly carry on long stories and monologues, often with strange personal adventures and extraordinary events; build up a fictional world. Describe funny stories of stupid, undignified, ridiculous, unbelievable situations; demonstrate a capacity of getting in and out of stupid situations.
5. Use burlesque as a source of humor.
6. Imitate in a ridiculous manner.
7. Mock, parody and lampoon teachers before their faces.
8. Distort customary rituals, such as serious ceremonies; provide a counterpoint to serious ceremonies; disrupt routines.

9. Satire social customs; react against extreme ritualization.
10. Horseplay.

Few students of the '60s counterculture would have come in contact with the remote world of the Yaqui clown allegorized in *The Teachings* had they not been seduced into it and "turned on" to it by Castaneda's beguiling exotic subject material: the esoteric wisdom of Yaqui drug use. Castaneda goaded turned-on students of the '60s into the secular world of the Yaqui clown in *The Teachings* with trappings of peyote, jimson weed, magic mushroom dust, hallucinatory visions, parapsychology, sorcery, magic and mysticism. Drawing upon ethnography studies of cargo cults in 1972, American professor of religion Daniel C. Noel characterized the psychedelic counter culture revitalization movement of the late '60s and early '70s that digested the secret teachings of don Juan as a "cargo culture."

Carlos Castaneda's 1968 book, *The Teachings of Don Juan*, set the stage for the neo-shamanism movement in modern America. The nomadic Yaqui Indian shaman don Juan introduced in *The Teachings* was the classic neo-shaman transference figure of a Mesoamerican pharmacological cargo cult. In 1977 Castaneda informed his readers in his fifth book that don Juan's teachings were Toltec teachings. Don Juan Matus was an oral bearer of a Toltec cargo cult. *The Teachings of Don Juan* allegedly revealed secret knowledge of a Toltec mystery tradition, a transpersonal Mesoamerican revitalization movement that had been driven underground in the Spanish conquest of Mexico. The esoteric shamanistic tradition revealed in *The Teachings* was a counterfeit Mesoamerican pharmacological cargo cult, a construct of the Pascola world. Don Juan Matus was a Spanish pseudonym for an "**old masked man**," a Yaqui *Pascola*. Spurious ethopharmacological data on smoke-inhaled Psilocybe mushroom dust in the syncretistic content of *The Teachings* forced readers of sha-manism to differentiate exoteric and esoteric knowledge. Adopting an oral technique used by Yaqui clowns to induct their audience into their world, Castaneda exploited the trappings of the collective in the '60s into the fictional world of the Pascola. Psychedelic readers and vicarious sorcerer apprentices unconsciously entered an allegorized world of the Yaqui Pascola clown in *The Teachings* through a counter-feit psychedelic cargo cult entrance.

In the years from 1960 to 1967 that Castaneda took to construct the fictional spiritual world of Yaqui psychedelic shamanism in *The Teachings*, the UCLA graduate anthropol-ogy student did little ethnohistorical research on the tribal religions of masked-clown societies among Mesoamerican Indians of post-conquest Mexico. Instead of painstakingly reconstructing the lost religious world of sacred clowns of Mesoamerica as an historical ethnographer, the Bruin anthro-pology student labored to disguise the cultural milieu of the secular Yaqui clown as an occult fiction writer. Conjuring an ethnomethodological "breaching" test to initiate anthropol-ogy students into the anomalous secular world of the Yaqui clown, Castaneda neglected to take into account the ethno-historical fact that Toltec-descended masked-clown societies of post-conquest Mexico had themselves devised cargo cult "breachings" tests in sacred texts to guide the future revital-ization of their tradition and protect it against detraditionalization by outside occult dabblers. As an ethnomethodologist an-thropologist of secular Mesoamerican clowns, Carlos Castaneda failed to get inside the heads of Mesoamerican sacred clowns that he allegorized in his books in the guise of shamans. Anthropologists universally distinguished Maria Sabina as a Mexican shamaness, but it should be remembered that the most famous woman shaman in the world also repeatedly identified herself in her chants as a sacred clown.

In his 1976 book *Castaneda's Journey*, Richard de Mille stated Robert Gordon Wasson's 1957 collector's book *Mushrooms, Russia and History* was what put him on the right track to unmasking Castaneda as a trickster. The don Juan debunker theorized that Castaneda's hallucinogenic mushroom dust, humito ("little smoke"), was inspired from previously published literary references written by Wasson that described Maria Sabina's preparatory purification rite of passing fungi through the smoke of burning aromatic plants. In the alleglossary to his 1980 book *The Don Juan Papers,* de Mille reiterated his theory that Castaneda's references to smoking mushrooms were adopted from Wasson's writings. De Mille cited the spurious Juanist practice of smoking mushrooms in *The Don Juan Papers* ten times (1980: 22-23, 42, 48, 58, 310, 320, 345, 429-430, 434, 440).

In 1984 I identified the probably inspirational literary source of Castaneda's "little smoke" in a Mesoamerican ethnomycology paper submitted to the *Journal of Psychoactive Drugs.* Castaneda's idea of smoking magic mushroom dust was not inspired from Maria Sabina's mushroom rites but from a joke, an act of clowning, published in U.C. Berkeley's off-campus underground hippie newspaper the *Berkeley Barb* in march 1967. The widely publicized smoking banana hoax of Spring 1967 was the inspiration for Castaneda's smoking mushroom hoax. Castaneda's magic mushroom dust smoke in *The Teachings* allegorized the American psychedelic counterculture banana peel dust joke of March 1967. The anthropologist's description of the hallucinogenic effects of magic mushroom smoke as "gentle" mirrored the fictitious hallucinogenic effects of banana smoke reported by young naive drug experimenters in *Newsweek* magazine (April 10, 1967).

Among the literary references to fungi Wasson cited in his 1957 ethnomycology book was a German reference to hallucinogenic mushrooms as "fungus of fools." According to an American experimenter of intoxicating fungi, quoted in Wasson's 1957 book, some of the effects of inebriated mushrooms were a desire to joke, speak foolishly and talk inordinantly; i.e., to talk like a clown. Spanish priests of southern Mexico identified Mesoamerican clowns as babblers, accomplished, witty, fluent speakers and social critics. In the 1960s, foreign magic mushroom seekers, like Henry Munn, visited Huautla de Jimenez, Oaxaca, Mexico, and discovered that all of the Mazatec mushroom shamans called the sacred mushroom clowns. In the late 1960s, Mexican journalist Fernando Benitez interviewed Marina Sabina and learned through a Mazatec interpreter that the famous mushroom shamaness-seer identified fungi as payosos, "clowns." Benitez published his interview of Maria Sabina in a book entitled *Los Indios de Mexico*, printed in Mexico in 1970. The Mazatec shamanic identification of sacred mushrooms as sacred clowns may have induced Castaneda to emphasize the role of hallucinogenic mushrooms in don Juan's teachings in his 1971 book *A Separate Reality*. Castaneda said all of the drug experiences in his second book were induced by smoking psilocybin mushrooms. The purpose of smoking mushrooms in don Juan's teachings was to help Carlos learn to "see." Ethnopharmacologists Steven Pollock and Ron Siegel documented in the *Journal of Psychedelic Drugs* in 1975 and 1981 that Psilocybe mushrooms are inactive when smoked. The pharmacological data against smoking magic mushroom dust suggests humito was introduced in the don Juan books as an allegorical device to teach apprentices to "see" the sacred mushrooms as clowns.

In co-opting the transpersonal quest of the psychedelic revitalization movement of the '60s to advance ethnomethodology, Castaneda gave little serious thought to the possibility that serious American counterculture seekers of profound ("heavy") mysticism, betwixt and between the worlds of *The*

Teachings, could breach the anomalous world of the Yaqui clown through a genuine Toltec cargo cult entrance Mesoamerican secular scientific anthropologists had overlooked in esoteric sacred texts. Ghost Dance pathfinders of Mexico's Trembling Instrument Tribe could enter the Toltec world of the Yaqui clown through the ceremonial specialist's dance costume mask and bells.

The present-day Yaqui Indians of Arizona and Sonors, Mexico retain only a few ritual costume vestiges of the most important pharmacological cult of pre-Colombian Mexico. Performing the role of a passage rite specialist in Yaqui culture with no connection to a ceremonial society, the modern pascola is culturally linked to extinct drug-adjuncted masked-clown societies of Toltec Mexico. Syncretizing elements from European culture, Yaqui clowns have lost many of the native traditions that were once connected to Mesoamerica's foremost pharmacological cult. The modern mask of Yaqui Pascola dancers is linked with the goat, yet goats were not native to Mesoamerica in pre-Hispanic time. The pre-Hispanic *nagual* cult animal of Mexico that was the prototype of the mask is a Toltec mystery to Yaqui Pascolas. The Yaqui Indian seer don Juan left these kinds of ethnohistorical mysteries in Castaneda's seventh book lost in Toltec world time.

The most important Toltec clown ritual costume motif worn by the modern Yaqui clown dancer are bells. Koyolim, the Yaqui term ascribed to the pascola's bell-belt, is a Nahuatl word that literally means "bells." Given the fact that the Aztecs used this same word and that Mesoamerican sacred books document that the ancient Yaquis called their god Yolcuat Quitzalcuat, the god of the Toltecs, there is strong linguistic evidence for advancing a Toltec connection with the Yaquis. According to a historical footnote published in Richard de Mille's 1980 book, American anthropologists dissuaded the Yaqui Indians of Arizona from advancing a Toltec connection in the 1960s (de Mille, 1980:433). The metal bells worn on the leather belts of Yaqui Indian clowns today in ceremonial dances are unique. The Yaquis appear to be the only Mesoamerican Indians who have retained the ancient Toltec dance tradition of wearing cascabels. The number of bells (7) worn by Yaqui clown dancers is of symbolic significance. The pre-Hispanic pharmacological cult that the dancing bells were once connected with is a Toltec mystery to modern Yaqui Pascola clown dancers.

In 1935 French artist Antonin Artaud (1896-1948) read published translations of Mesoamerican books of secret doctrine while living in Paris. These sacred texts, written by native Indians in post-conquest time, described the use of bells in ceremonial rites and the role of dancing bells in a prophetic religious cargo cult of a Toltec-descended masked men's secret society called the Trembling Instrument Tribe. Having access to only very poor translations of the esoteric texts, the French occult seeker of Mesoamerican mysticism never learned that part of the shamanic books secretly described a native Indian conspired entheogenic honey cult revitalization movement in post-conquest southern Mexico.

Tantalized by anthropology references to shamanic dances performed by Mexican Indians in magical peyote rites, Artaud left France in 1936 for Mexico to immerse himself in the Mexico mystique and to seek out the old secrets of Mexican Indian magic medicine. Artaud's mystical goal was to establish a connection with a Mesoamerican revitalization movement he believed was dawning in Mexico. The French occult explorer hoped to export rediscovered secrets of ancient Mexican Indian magic to France and make them available to the country's post-Surrealist artists seeking the "intense spirituality" of lost esoteric traditions. Like Carlos Castaneda's revitalization of a pre-Colombian mystical tradition in the '60s, Antonin Artaud sought to revitalize a secret magical system in Mexico from peyote sorcerers. Castaneda's initiation to Yaqui Indian sorcery in *The Teachings* imitated Artaud's initiation into Mexican Indian sorcery in the 1930s. The occult quest to obtain shamanic power over the diabolic world through the ritual ingestion of magical peyote in *The Teachings* was the same quest French artist Antonin Artaud described in his 1936 essay *The Peyote Dance*. Castaneda's leading critic, Richard de Mille, briefly mentioned in his 1980 book *The Don Juan Papers* that a number of American anthropologists in the '70s noted striking similarities between Artaud's memoir and Castaneda's story (de Mille, 1980:395).

The most noteworthy ethnohistorical reference of Indian magic lore to be gleaned from Artaud's 1936 account of peyote cult rites among the Tarahumara Indians of northern Mexico is the artist's description of dancing bells. The psychedelic explorer had the fortune of seeing an ancient shamanic costume motif that later modern ethnographers and peyote seekers of northern Mexico would never encounter in the 1960s. Artaud saw a Tarahumara shaman in a peyote dance leap into the air with six hundred bells. Three hundred of the bells were made of silver. The French Surrealist artist never rediscovered and revitalized the secrets of pre-Colombian Mesoamerican ecstatic shamanism in Mexico, but he did leave his readers a classic description of psychedelic synesthesia.

Artaud metaphorically described the peyote dancer's costume as an "army of bells" (de Mille, 1980:109). The clamorous sound of these bells evoked in Artaud's collective unconscious a subjective sensation of a tempestuous disorder of mad swarming bees caked together. The psychedelic-intoxicated French poet had no conscious knowledge that ancient Toltec-descended Indians of the Trembling Instrument Tribe of southern Mexico had ritually used magic noise, of drums and bells in pre-Hispanic time, to induce honey-bees to swarm. Unable to understand the esoteric meaning of sacred Mesoamerican texts, Artaud never learned that the metal dancing bells he saw in northern Mexico were culturally linked to an ancient secret Toltec magical beekeeping tradition. Trembling instrument Tribe religious acculturation specialists of post-conquest Mexico revealed metal bells were the leading musical instrument motif of a revitalization movement. Cascabels were the heralding instrument of a prophetic psychedelic honey cargo cult.

Mesoamerican Indians, practicing the shamanic art of metallurgy in central Mexico, had cast copper bells for centuries by the lost-wax method. Mexican smiths obtained their wax from the beehives of native stingless bees that Indians domesticated for entheogenic honey. Psychoactive lysergic acid amide honey was rediscovered by this writer through ethnobotany research at UCLA in 1981. The ancient secret society identity of the honey plant from which entheogenic honey was produced was rediscovered in the early 1980s through deciphering esoteric Mesoamerican shamanic texts. The name of the *nagual* cult animal identified with the name of the Mesoamerican shamanic plant was solved through linguistic research. Ethnobotany experts have ethnographically misidentified the *nagual* cult name of the shamanic plant since the 16th century.

Lost-beeswax cast precious metal-plated copper bells played an important far-flung trade and cult role in the sacred honey bee culture of pre-Colombian Mexico. Copper *nagual* skull effigy bells are the most unique archaeological treasures of Mesoamerica's entheogenic honey cult. Lost-beeswax cast Toltec nectar bells are so strongly identified with heralding the revival of Mexico's extinct entheogenic honey cult in esoteric books of the Clamoring Language of the Trembling Instrument Tribe revitalization movement could be called the "Cascabel Cargo Cult."

According to an Arizona tourist guidebook on Yaqui Indian dance ceremonies published in 1960, the sounds of jingling bells, at the commencement of the Yaqui Easter ceremonies, herald the entrance of the Pascolas. Sacred Mesoamerican books on Toltec Indian dances written in post-conquest Mexico prophecized that the clamorous sound of bells in another time would herald the entrance of the Trembling Instrument Tribe.

Selected Bibliography

Beals, Ralph L. 1943 *The Aboriginal Culture of the Cahita Indians.* University of California Press. masked-down societies, 70; the pascola and shamanism, 70.

Beals, Ralph L. and Parsons, Elsie Clews 1934 "The Sacred Clowns of the Pueblo and Mayo-Yaqui Indians," *American Anthropologist,* Vol. 36, No. 4, 491-514.

Crapanzano, Vincent 1973 "Popular Anthropology," *Partisan Review,* Vol. 40, No. 3, 471-482. clowning, 477, 479; clowns, 479-482.

de Mille, Richard, ed. 1980 *The Don Juan Papers: Further Castaneda Controversies.* Ross-Erikson Publishers. Karlosla, 85.

Laska, Vera 1959 "Seeking Life," *Memoirs of the American Folklore Society,* Vol. 50. Pueblo clowns, 13-15.

Noel, Daniel C. 1976 *Seeing Castaneda: Reactions to the "Don Juan" Writings of Carlos Castaneda.* Capricorn Books. G. P. Putnam's Sons.

Painter, Murial Thayer 1986 *With Good Heart. Yaqui Beliefs and Ceremonies in Pascua Village.* University of Arizona Press. Edward H. Spicer, ed., pascola "language," 242, 269-271; pascola clowning, 267; pascola bells, 245; shamanistic power, 267; enchanted goat, 247.

Spicer, Edward Holland 1940 *Pascua, A Yaqui in Sonora.* University of Chicago Press. pascola "language," 186-189; pascolas and the devil, 196-197, 202, pascola name, 174.

1954 *Potam, A Yaqui Village in Sonora.* American Anthropological Association Memoir No. 7. pascola specialists, 76-77; patterns of ritual, 155; ritual satire, 172-174; pascola arts, 183-184.

1961 *Perspectives in American Indian Cultural Change.* University of Chicago Press. pascola oral literature, 63.

1980 *The Yaquis. A Cultural History.* University of Arizona Press. pascola clowning, 105; pascola "language," 106, 108-110.

FURTHER COMMENTS ON U4Euh, WITH MORE RECENT ADDENDA

by Thomas Lyttle

There are two classic papers presently being circulated in the underground, or among those purchasing illegal or not officially approved versions of U4Euh, Intellex or 4-Methyl-Aminorex. These periodically revised papers, authored by The Friendly Stranger, are *U4Euh*, a four-page flyer and *What Happened When the Friendly Stranger Introduced U4Euh* at four to six pages in flyer form. Both are offset or photocopied and stamped, usually in red ink. with the words **NOT for PUBLICATION or PUBLIC DISCLOSURE** over the main text in various spots. After conferencing with the Friendly Stranger, it has been decided that at this time the information contained in both these instructional manuals should remain private and available only to those actively involved in legitimate archiving, legal pharmacology or medical practices in countries allowing for U4Euh's prescription.

Recent mystifications regarding U4Euh have been potentiated in popular press articles in *The Whole Earth Review* (Summer 1988), *Street Pharmacologist* (SP)(Dec. 1987) and elsewhere.

The following letter from *The Friendly Stranger* is reproduced in response to the *SP* (N.I.D.A.)-sponsored article. For the sake of clarity and continuity, both the short *SP* piece is reproduced verbatim, as is the *FS* (Friendly Stranger) letter of response.

From *Street Pharmacologist*, (December 1987):

The Ice Man Cometh

A new clandestine, synthetic drug has been reported in Florida. **Ice,** also known as **U4Euh** on the street, is synthesized from phenylpropanolamine (PPA), a central nervous system stimulant, and cyanogen bromide, a derivative of the poisonous gas, cyanide. The chemical name of Ice (U4Euh) is 4-methyl aminorex.

Aminorex was researched as a diet aid between the 1950s and 1960s. McNeil Laboratories received a patent and began testing it in 1964. Aminorex was subsequently shelved because its stimulant properties were too potent.

When taken at lower doses, Ice produces amphetamine-like effects. A hallucinogenic effect, similar to PCP, occurs at higher doses.

Some drug dealers are marketing Ice as cocaine or crystal methampetamine. Ice may be taken in powder or liquid form. Most users snort it or mix it in a drink. A small percentage of users administer it intravenously. Florida law enforcement officials have identified approximately 15 cases in central and northeast Florida involving the powdered drug.

The first documented overdose fatally occurred in 1986. A 37-year-old male with a history of clandestine chemical manufacturing was found dead in a Florida hotel room. A plastic bag containing white powder was discovered in his pocket. the bag was labeled "4-methyl aminorex free base. Not for injection. For sacramental use only." An autopsy report confirmed the cause of death to be a drug overdose.

As a result, the DEA classified Ice as a Schedule 1 drug on October 15, 1987. Prior to the emergency scheduling, a clandestine lab was seized in Pennsylvania where Ice was manufactured. A Gainesville, Florida lab was seized after Ice was banned. The state of Florida outlawed the substance in 1986.

—SK

Case Report: A Fatality Involving U4Euh. Orlando Crime Laboratory.
Gwen Love: *Corner Drug Store.* Gainesville, FL
Merck Index, Tenth Edition

The following is The Friendly Stranger's response to *Street Pharmacologist* - which they apparently refused to print.

In Defense of U4Euh

You have seen only the bad side of U4Euh, so I can understand your yellow journalism. I can understand it, but I do not forgive it. Yes, it is made from a "stimulant" and a "poison." But common table salt is composed of sodium and chlorine, both of which are poisonous.

Aminorex was withdrawn, at least in Europe, because it caused degenerative pulmonary hypertension after *prolonged, daily* use. Possibly due to the methyl group, we have detected no similar tendency in U4Euh.

As for "amphetamine-like effects," you could have used a neutral term like "alpha-adrenergic effects," but NOOOooo...Doesn't every "stimulant" (another buzz word) produce "Amphetamine-like effects?" What about caffeine? As for "hallucinogenic effect" on "higher doses," how much higher? VERY MUCH higher—ENORMOUS overdoses. Were the hallucinations caused by it, or by a lack of sleep? The recommended amount is ten to twenty-five milligrams, maximum of fifty milligrams, not more than once a week. "...similar to PCP"—another buzz word.

Yes, I am bothered that people misrepresent it. KNOW YOUR DEALER! "A small percentage of users administer it intravenously." HOW small a percentage? Obviously, if it was a large percentage, you'd include a number. A "small percentage" of needle freaks will shoot *anything*. Only a small percentage shoot U4Euh because needle freaks prefer the rush from speed. "nobody that (sic) can get meth likes it." (anon.)

"The first...fatality"—have there been *other* deaths, or was that the ONLY one? Considering how much there may be out there, only one fatality would tend to indicate its relative safety. That fatality had reportedly been using it *one or more times every day for several months,* and taking phenobarb to sleep. He would gobble almost anything he could get his hands on. "...a history of clandestine chemical manufacturing"...ONE *conviction*..."cause of death to be a drug overdose." A drug. *What* drug? Did U4Euh *cause* it, did something else cause it, or was it the synergistic effect of several substances? Exactly *what* did the autopsy show? That he lived as long as did, despite such outrageous abuse of it, is proof of its relative safety.

This is, of necessity, anonymous. To paraphrase Miranda, anything you write can and damned well WILL be used against you if the Pigs want to. I could send you copies of the *many* favorable reports on U4Euh including the basic four-page brochure if I have your assurance they will not be published and will not fall into the hands of the Pigs.

I am going to make what you will consider an outrageous suggestion: the next time you get a pure sample of it, try some. Only then will you know. Read the comments about it in the Winter 1987 *Whole Earth Review*.

The title was clever, but how did it get the name Ice? I KNOW how it got the name U4Euh.

This is a photocopy, made on a public machine, and was handled using gloves. The envelope was sealed and the stamp applied using water, not identifiable saliva.

—The Friendly Stranger

The long letter regarding U4Euh printed in *Whole Earth Review* (no. 59, Summer 1988) was in response to their previous Winter 1987 piece by "R. U. Sirius" of *High Frontiers* magazine which accidentally (?) gave U4Euh the chemical structure for another drug, MDA, which is dissimilar in effects.

The nomenclature for U4Euh therein was given as 3,4 Methylenedimethoxy Methamphetamine which the letter's author showed as "an impossible chemical structure."

Without stretching this point too far, other "points of fact" laid down in the response letter included "like crystal methedrine, it is almost certainly capable of precipitating paranoid psychosis," and "Finally, *U4Euh* is relatively untested, both scientifically and on the street," and so on. The implications of "brain damage, kidney damage, heart damage and liver damage" continue the barrage. Here is the Friendly Stranger's unprinted response to "May You Never Sleep—Cognition Enhancing Drugs" from *The Whole Earth Review.*

Feedback on Cognitive Activators from The Friendly Stranger

I was one of the first half-dozen or so people to enjoy U4Euh. I also named it. That's a brand name. Clever? I thought so.

Someone else suggested the name Intellex. The description in the box is TOTALLY incorrect. I doubt that R. U. Sirius was guilty of so egregious an error. If he was, he completely destroyed his credibility.

U4Euh does NOT fit the definition of "designer drug"; it was created decades before the term was thought up, and it lay hidden in a journal article and patent. Calling it a "stimulant" plays into the hands of DEA pigs and Nancy et al. Saying it is "chemically related to MDMA" is like saying that a Model T Ford is structurally related to a Formula One Ferrari. U4Euh is related to MDMA *only* in that both contain a benzene ring and are composed of Carbon, Oxygen, Hydrogen, and Nitrogen. There are tens, possibly hundreds, of *thousands* of compounds which fit that description. It IS similar to Pemoline. No, I am NOT going to reveal its exact molecular structure or chemical name. Why should I?

I feel somewhat like the way John Sutter may have felt after word about the discovery of gold leaked out. U4Euh was already out, in Florida, so it was possibly only a matter of time. But my introduction of it at a major gathering of free spirits, ex-hippies, "freaks," etc., to put it politely, resulted in it getting out to California where the "baby birds" *continued* to disobey instructions and take too much of it, unnecessarily winding up at the Haight-Ashbury Clinic. The DEA pigs learned about it and it was Emergency Scheduled.

Mea Culpa. Partly. I did the best I could with what I knew at the time. If I knew then what I know now, I would NOT have been so generous, would NOT have identified it, and would have required that people take it in my presence. My lack of academic credentials notwithstanding, I am attempting to be a responsible researcher. If I used the term "professional," someone would interpret that as "drug dealer," wouldn't they? It was the first time in fifteen (15!) years that someone included descriptive literature with a "new" substance. Obviously none of the several hundreds of four-page brochures I gave out ever reached R. U. Sirius. I requested written feedback. When I got none, I had to demand it. "No more U4Euh until I get a report." I have since prepared a generic experience report form.

"It's not paranoia when they really ARE after you." After I got a nice reply to my first letter to the leading psychopharmacological chemist, my second letter to him was opened in the mail in the Post Office where I mailed it. Three photocopied pages disappeared. He is too well known. DO NOT print his name. He values his privacy. An audio tape from the editor of a small circulation journal about psychedelics was "lost in the mail." And never found, of course. I phoned (from a coin phone, of course!) the editor of the *J. Psychoactive Drugs* and he told me he never got the letter I'd sent him. No, it did NOT include that name in the address. I DO eventually learn from my mistakes.

I have also been ignored. I sent an info package to "a leading authority in the field." No reply. I hand-delivered a similar package to *the* Timothy Leary. No reply. I met the author of a well-known book about LSD and we chatted and exchanged phone numbers. He didn't return my call. I notified *High times* four—FOUR—(4!) times. Executive Editor Dean Latimer told me they didn't want to know anything about it until it made the media elsewhere. When it was Scheduled, I reminded them of my involvement with it. "We already have a story about it." "You don't want any more information??!" "No." *Nothing* has appeared in H.T.

I was (unnecessarily, it turned out) concerned about possible long-term harmful effects of it. An analog had caused a fatal disease but apparently the difference in molecular structure eliminated this, for I have had NO reports of any permanent negative effects. I should have gone out to CA, gone into massive production, dumped all I could before it was Scheduled, and converted the proceeds into Real Money— the kind that doesn't burn or inflate—Gold and Silver. Now that it's Scheduled, I am suddenly committing a felony. somehow I doubt that the pigs would accept my "grandfather clause" defense. Or the "religious sacrament" defense.

So I consider Kevin Kelly, of the *Whole Earth Review*, naive: "I bet there is a reputation to be made by a scientist who could lift this out of the outlaw realm into controlled lab science." It all *starts* in the lab (read the journals) and if it's any good, it gets out of the lab, and eventually the pigs and Puritans outlaw it. Look at history. How many compounds have been outlawed? As they say, "This is left as an exercise for the student."

Don't you remember when the Food and Drug Gestapo tried to require an Rx to buy vitamins in bulk? They did achieve some Newspeak: Minimum Daily Requirement became Recommended Daily Allowance. "Allowance," as if we are children. Could it be they don't want people to be too healthy? As Pearson and Shaw point out in *Life Extension*, the Social [in] Security System is bankrupt and if people live longer it will only get more bankrupt.

"They've got the guns but we've got the numbers." And what are we doing with our numbers? Nothing. Paying our taxes (what did Thoreau say?) and feeding a Cancer. Fighting among ourselves, or sitting around, shrugging. Liberals support the First Amendment but not the Right to Defend Oneself (as if an ACLU membership card could stop a rapist) and Conservatives, vice versa. "I don't want to waste my vote by voting Libertarian" so (maybe) you vote for Tweedledee or Tweedledum, and when either of them wins by more than one vote, your vote WAS wasted. Or "Don't vote; you just encourage them." Although there appears to be much truth in "If voting could change The System, voting would be illegal." Look what's happening to the Jury's Right to Nullify the Law (the right to decide the law as well as the facts) which goes back to ancient English common law. End of Sermon.

My experiences with most of the "wonnerful" substances described in the article have been disappointing.
And I'm not the only one. The "lines" are: "the effects
are subtle"; "You have to take it for months," and then
when you still don't notice any effect, "Well, you must be
one of those people who get no benefit from it."
Remember "B vitamins will restore color to grey hair?"
Maybe not—you're probably too young. Now they admit
it works for only a very small percentage of people.

Regarding the following:

Hydergine: I agree with an MD friend's opinion of it: "Only
effect I could detect was that it lightened my wallet." I said
Goodbye to a Ben Franklin. Yes, I would take it before
surgery or some high-risk sport like SCUBA diving or skiing
(where I might be buried in an avalanche) for its "the brain
can survive without oxygen for thirty minutes instead of five"
benefit, but that's all.

Deaner: "Subtle." Too subtle for me. I could probably drink it
like water but water costs less.

Pemoline: It's surprising how different some close relatives
can be (But then, considering how different close human
relatives can be, I shouldn't be surprised). It lasted three or
four hours and produced no feeling of euphoria, just an
annoying "busy" feeling in my head.

Lecithin: I seemed to perk up the first time I used it and have
remained at that level. I use it with vegetable oil to cook eggs
and potatoes and onions.

PRL 8-53: If you read Pearson carefully, he describes two
peoples' experiences with it. I doubt he's tried it. Lack of
consistency of effects is a major problem with substances. I
haven't tried it yet, but if it does work, WOW! What will the
Pigs be able to say as a justification for scheduling it? Maybe
"It gives the people who take it an unfair advantage over
those who don't."

One substance did produce a totally serendipitous effect on me. It reduced my sleep requirement from seven or eight hours to four hours, with no detectable side effects. I woke fully refreshed and literally could not sleep any longer. I SPECULATE, and I emphasize SPECULATE, that it altered my acetylcholine level. What is it? Hah! I may be crazy, but I'm not stupid. Maybe someday you'll get lucky and be approached by The Friendly Stranger.

Oh yes, the four-page brochure about U4Euh. Should I give you permission to reprint it? What effect will that have? Probably encourage people to seek it, and encourage every would-be bathtub chemist to come out of the woodwork and possibly kill himself with the highly toxic compound used to make it.

This is an all-or-nothing offer: print every word of the above or none at all. The Pigs won't sue you because I call them Pigs, and you wouldn't capitalize ee cummings poetry, would you? So leave my capitals and spelling AS IS. I'm still micturated off at your ancestors over a few reviews in the Various Whole Earth Catalogs. "Don't confuse us with facts; we've already made up our minds; that was a friend of mine who reviewed that."

7-88

From the community-at-large comes many interesting anecdotal accounts. The following is excerpted from *Psychedelic Monographs and Essays* (Spring 1988) Letter section.

...Recently met someone who was distributing a drug called U4Euh or Intellex at the 1986 Continental Rainbow Gathering in Pennsylvania. He gave us a pile of brochures regarding this substance. Let me say that for the record, his 'pushing' of this synthetic stimulant—an unholy sacrament—created what many characterized as "severe problems." This consequently was met with or followed by decidedly more negative feelings than positive.

Basically, when combined with LSD, too many bad, violent trips occurred.

I am in touch with key individuals and we would like to submit a review regarding U4Euh as I understand you are considering running other literature about U4Euh in a future issue. The general feeling was that the Rainbow distributor engaged in widespread recklessness, irresponsibility and casual experimentation which some saw as a "disaster."

However, I personally thought that the literature being distributed by this person was "excellent to brilliant."

Here is *The Friendly Stranger's* response:

I am tempted to claim that *The Friendly Stranger* and U4Euh never happened; we were all a mass hallucination caused by overdoses of LSD.

"Drug" is a "four-letter word" and using the term plays into the hands of DEA and other pigs and Nancy et al. Ditto "stimulant."

I did not "push" U4Euh. I offered it. If I "pushed" anything, I pushed information. People were Free To Choose.

As for "synthetic", I am so tired of "natural", "organic" nuts and flakes who refuse to accept facts. A molecule is the same whether it is created in a plant or animal or in laboratory glassware. LSD is semi-synthetic and strychnine is natural. Does that mean that LSD is bad and strychnine is good?

Who the Hell are you (**or is ANYONE**) to declare U4Euh (**or ANYTHING**) "unholy"?? Bigotry is why religious wars occur.

It is virtually impossible to completely foolproof anything. Foolproof: to make proof against fools. Only a complete fool takes ANYTHING for the first time WITH something else, ESPECIALLY with something as powerful as LSD.

Thank you for the compliment re the literature. We (mostly I) put a lot of effort into it. It's not my fault that Damn Fool Baby Birds refused to read it. At the start, I made certain people understood it and I quizzed them, but I was eventually inundated by requests. THEY were the ones who "engaged in widespread recklessness, irresponsibility and casual experimentation which some saw as a 'disaster'".

I must admit I don't remember you. There were so many camps. Where was yours?

The Friendly Stranger

Two pertinent and even more recent papers from the medical and legal communities also should be included regarded U4Euh. These are in complement to the list given by The New Age Chemist, which focuses more on tracing early references and this compound's creation in the early 1960s.

The first document is the *Department of Justice (DEA)* scheduling report which made U4Euh (called therein 2-Amino-4-methyl-5-phenyl-2-oxazoline) illegal on August 13, 1987. This three-page, single-spaced report reviews the legal ramifications of the original 1984 CSA (*Controlled Substances Act*) which allows for the DEA to place, in emergency situations pertaining to imminent public safety, *any* old or new drug or compound, or chemically based object or living thing, onto Schedule 1, as was done with U4Euh at that time. This paper also reviews some of the initial findings taken from the primary sources listed in The New Age Chemist's piece, plus detailed reports of illegal labs as well as the report of one death related to U4Euh. The complete title of this paper is: *21 CFR Part 1308; Schedules of Controlled Substances; Temporary Placement of 2-Amino-4-methyl-5-phenyl-2-oxazoline (4-methyl-Aminorex) Into Schedule 1; 52 FR 30174; August 13, 1987.*

For further information contact: H. McClain, Jr., Chief, Drug Control Section, DEA, Washington, D.C. 20537; telephone 1-202-633-1366.

The Journal of Forensic Sciences more recently printed a piece called *A Fatality Involving U4Eub, A Cyclic Derivative of Phenylpropanolamine* by Davis & Brewster, two Florida-based researchers. This appeared in the Vol. 33, No. 2, March 1988 edition.

The brief abstract presented is as follows:

A fatality involving ingestion of diazepan and 4,5-dihydro-4-methyl-5-phenyl-2-oxazoline, a cyclic derivative of phenylpropanolamine known as U4Euh were analyzed using gas chromatography, ultraviolet and infrared spectroscopy, nuclear magnetic resonance, and mass spectrometry. Physiologic fluids were analyzed quantitatively by gas chromatography and qualitatively by gas-chromatography-mass-spectrometry. Concentrations of 4,5-dihydro-4-methyl-5-phenyl-2-oxazolamine were: in blood: 21.3 mg./L.; in urine: 12.3 mg./L. Diazepam concentration in blood was 0.8 mg./L.

It is certain that as this substance U4Euh becomes more well-known, further scientific and underground publishing will be the result. Having whatever facts-of-the-matter exist so far as published information seems the proper prerequisite for any intelligent survey of U4Euh and its future modifications.

WHERE THE
PANTAGRUELION GROWS

by Ben G. Price

In fine, Ludes omniform are these invented
And every Indoles and sense contented.
Pleasure invades, Pain abdicates the Mind.
What more in Heav'n can its grand Tenants find!
—Francois Rabelais

Francois Rabelais (1494–1553), author of *Gargantua and Pantagruel,* would well be considered the patron saint of wine, women and song, yielding nothing to the god of these virtues, Bacchus. In literary circles he is well remembered for his lusty praise of the drunken art. But to the list of things he blessed must be added the hedonic enjoyment of the plant cannabis sativa, better known as marijuana.

Little support for such a view will be found in extant criticisms of Rabelais' acclaimed work, and it's really not surprising. Rabelais lived in a restrictive society with certain phobias in common with our own, although the provocation of such popular phobias protected ecclesiastical authority in his day, whereas they protect secular authority in our own.

In a restrictive society wherein certain ways of thinking, certain topics, certain beliefs, or even curiosity about the legitimacy of consensus perceptions is taboo (a circumstance ostensibly "impossible" in a scientific, rationalist culture like ours), an independent thinker is left with three alternatives if he has a desire to express unpopular ideas: 1) self-censorship; 2) open violation of the taboo; 3) cryptic propagation of his ideas.

Self-censorship and bucking the system tend to accomplish the same undesirable goal: silence is imposed either by the self or someone else. But a little guile and a little showmanship goes a long way towards freeing-up the communication of non-cliche ideas. Witness the "underground" rock music of the '60s. (Admittedly, the realization by social sycophants that they had been had has caused them to become paranoid hysterics over supposed "satanic" influences and drug-related subliminal hypnotic suggestion.)

Francois Rabelais was in much the same position as were the musician experimenters in psychedelics of the 1960s. The "New World," America, was discovered and explored in his lifetime. "America" landed on the moon in 1969. The Spanish Inquisition was in full swing when Rabelais was a boy. For most "hippies" McCarthyism was a childhood memory. Rabelais reveled in hedonic bliss while Martin Luther defied the authority of the Roman Church. The "psychedelic revolution" attended the funeral of the first (and last) Catholic president, as well as public religion.

Gargantua and Pantagruel has long been respected as the epitome of irreverent satire. It is the amazing account of the life and wanderings of Gargantua and his son, Pantagruel, in which nothing is left sacred except life and the open enjoyment of it. And yet Rabelais kept some secrets, or at least he was cagey about what he revealed. But he knew his audience, and addressed them by way of introduction in this manner.

"Most illustrious Drinkers and you, most precious syphilitics, for it is to you and not to others that my writings are dedicated..."

As a free thinker not willing to risk his cherished well-being in a society hostile to what went on in his head, Rabelais chose to keep his thoughts private, but not unshared. He shared them with the rare individuals who, like himself, were undaunted by their own irreverence, and who were capable thereby of circumventing the rigid conventions of literary and grammatical tradition. Through an early form of surrealism, he conveyed his message to those who were not too rigid in their perceptions to understand it.

Of particular interest to us must be the most oblique segments of *Pantagruel*, Book III, chapters 49-52. For long periods these chapters were banned by the church, and in many modern translations of the Pantagruel they are omitted.

Gargantua and Pantagruel is not the kind of text that is popularly read. Like other "classic" bits of literature, it is spoon-fed to freshman college students in general literature classes. Seldom would it be dealt with by even marginally sophisticated literature majors. It is just not done. The few English translations of the work are clearly bad translations, or they are censored ones, such as the Viking edition, the *Portable Rabelais*, which is the most popular. Significantly, the chapters omitted from this edition are the very ones of interest to this discussion.

A synopsis of the omitted chapters rendered by Viking perhaps reveals more about the intellectual limitations of literary scholars than they have revealed about the works of great writers. The synopsis of the omitted chapters reads, in part:

"Book Third draws to a close with several enigmatic chapters on the plant called "Pantagruelion." The digression may have been suggested by the hempen sails of the Pantagruel's ship, although others see it as an allusion to the introduction and frequent use of the rope as a punishment for criminals during Francis I's reign. In any event, it is an extremely learned little essay, and a mystic-sounding one. for one reason or another, it is not unusual for Maitre Francois to begin or close his books with an "enigma" of this sort. There may have been a method to his madness—there usually was."

The suggestion of the frequent use of the hempen rope as punishment for crimes is a giveaway, of course. It is, essentially, the justification for continued censorship. But no synopsis can give the full content of Rabelais' message. No matter what the warning label, we ought to take a look at what he actually said, scholars be damned!

Let us be clear on this: hidden references to a mind-altering herb and its properties would appear to be genuinely Rabelaisian, given an understanding of the author and his character. The Viking edition of Rabelais censored certain chapters, adjudging them "the last Rabelaisian portions," as if they had not been written by him, although they undeniably were. Hence, just as in the time of Rabelais, some modern hyperbole of morality has found it Orwellianly possible to read an author and discover in his writings some magic bullet that discounts what he has written on psychological grounds (now that the religious grounds for heresy have been discredited).

Literary pedants and socially conscious scholars would like us to believe that Rabelais, as an example of literary genius, was ignorant of, rather than a proponent of, the more remarkable properties of the plant he called "Pantagruelion" after his protagonist, Pantagruel. But Rabelais clearly hinted to the contrary in his description of his renaming of the herb:

"It is likewise called Pantagruelion, because of the notable and singular qualities, virtues, and properties thereof. For as Pantagruel hath been the idea, pattern, prototype, and exemplary of all jovial perfection and accomplishment...so in this Pantagruelion have I found so much efficacy and energy, so much completeness and excellency, so much exquisiteness and rarity, and so many admirable effects and operations of a transcendental nature..."

In spite of scholarly myopia, Pantagruel's "Rabelaisian" character has attached itself to the herb he called Pantagruelion. True, there are segments in these chapters that seem to be dedicated to the praise of the herb as the source of gallows twine; they are unconvincing as such.

Speaking more openly of the more pleasant qualities of his favorite weed might have enraged the clergy, ever vigilant and anxious to "protect" Rabelais' soul from arcane evils, much as the medical mendicants of the American insurance industry have become adamant about "protecting" everybody's body and indemnifiable health. And so it is not surprising that the true message of *Pantagruel*, Book III has been obscured by a protective overlay in praise of more mundane qualities. It may not be surprising, also, that critics have had authentic difficulty in interpreting the significant chapters.

Despite the vicissitudes of his times, Rabelais did manage to impregnate his already baudy and blasphemous work with secret allusions to the psychoactive properties of cannabis sativa; yet it was much easier for him to openly speak of fellow drinkers. The Church could not readily condemn the use of alcohol while that drug played a major sacramental role in the observance of the Eucharist.

If there is any doubt that Rabelais used cryptography to mask his real intent, his "word to the wise" instructions should be read closely:

> "Following the dog's example, you will have to be wise in sniffing, smelling and estimating these fine and meaty books; swiftness in the chase and boldness in the attack are what is called for; after which, by careful reading and frequent meditation, you should break the bone and suck the substantific marrow... in the course of it you will find things of quite a different taste and a doctrine more abstruse which shall reveal to you most high sacraments and horrific mysteries in what concerns our religion, as well as the state of our political and economic life."

A significant portion of what Rabelais wrote in these chapters was so much fluff, intended to keep church officials off his back. With great sarcasm he wrote:

> "The Lord forbid, that we should use any fables in this a so veritable history... for Pantagruel was the inventor thereof. I do not say of the plant itself, but of a certain use which it serves for, exceeding odious and hateful to thieves and robbers."

Rabelais was essentially an atheist, and to the priests, bishops and pontiff filled the social role of "thieves and robbers," who with the sale of "indulgences" larded their ecclesiastical wealth. Thus it is not the hangman's noose that is found odious in this "certain use," as some literary critics would have it, but the rising rings of smoke that seem to get more close to fulfilling the heretical promise of gnosticism than established church doctrine would allow.

Modern misinterpretations of Rabelais are grounded in the inherited premises of the literary critics. Ignorance of church history has something to do with it. Rabelais got away with something; it is remarkable that his words have survived at all, even though they continue to be censored, even in translation, even in modern times.

In an atmosphere of repression and medieval theocracy not much different from the thick social overlay of Iranian repression in the 1980s, he engaged in an intrigue of words that satisfied the authorities as to the innocent nature of his botanical aside, which is the form these chapters ostensibly take. He nevertheless retained his sense of humor and derogatorily compared dope-smoking to the other Christian bugaboo, masturbation. Whereas the latter was touted to bring on blindness and madness, illicit toking was horrific in its own right because:

"It would quite extinguish the natural heat and procreative virtue of the semence of any man, who would each much, and often of it."

This passage might be modernized to read: Hash brownies will make you impotent, a claim which, in fact, is still being entertained by "serious" conservative scientists. Rabelais did not let the absurdity rest without embellishment. He continued, and through exaggeration made it clear that he was writing satire:

"It endangereth bad and unwholesome blood, and with its exorbitant heat woundeth them with grievous, hurtful, smart and noisome vapours."

In other words, Rabelais was gaffing, smoking grass will give you gas and make you fart!

Aside from this kind of satire, Rabelais gave aspiring cultivators useful information about the proper care and planting of cannabis. With customary obscurity the singular properties of the female plant were indicated by negating the female plant as totally useless, as "serviceable to little or no purpose." And yet, immediately following this condemnation, it is the female plant that is recommended for cultivation:

"This Pantagruelion is to be sown at the first coming of the swallows, and it is to be plucked out of the ground when the grasshoppers begin to be a little hoarse."

Despite the claims of scholars, in Europe by the end of the Middle Ages marijuana was valued for its hempen fibers, but also for its culinary and aphrodisiac properties:

"Without this herb, kitchens would be detested, the tables of dining rooms abhorred...and the choicest beds also, how richly soever adorned with gold, silver, amber, ivory, porphyry, and the mixture of most precious metals, would without it yield no delight or pleasure to the reposers in them."

A favorite "explanation" of the Pantagruelion chapters by scholars is the convoluted portrayal of the sotted author going on about hempen sails, the fabricated essence of European might-a-sea. Sort of like showing the anti-nuke demonstrator to be a closet sadist. A favorite propaganda technique of tyrants. Undeniably there is some reference to hempen sails in these chapters, but they must be taken in context:

"By the help thereof those remote nations, whom nature seemed unwilling to have discovered to us, and so desirous to keep them still 'in abscondito' and hidden from us, that the ways through which their countries were to be reached unto, were not only unknown, but judged also to be altogether impermeable and inaccessible, are now arrived to us, and we to them."

It's easy enough to overlook the transcendental nature of these Rabelaisian voyages, but to do so consistently in the name of pedant scholarship requires an agile allegiance to the status quo.

Rabelais foresaw this and satirized those who would keep their followers in ignorance for the sake of maintaining power over them. The "celestial intelligences," as Rabelais bitingly refers to the clergy, posed themselves as the mid-wives of the common man's hopeful entry into the transcendental realm called "heaven." This was the promised reward for unerring obedience to ecclesiastical authority, but it was to be bestowed, only after death.

In our time, the "expert intelligences" of medicine and "law" do the work of defanged clergymen. Speaking from their academic and bureaucratic pulpits, wielding sheepskins and gavels instead of crucifixes and miters, they pose themselves as the midwives of the common man's hopeful entry into the mundane realm of conformity.

Any clergy, whether secular or mythbound, will feel threatened by a perceptual tool which allows the common man to transcend conditioning and experience unmediated clarity. This is what Rabelais knew would happen to the medieval priests if he openly discussed the remarkable qualities of the plant, Pantagruel. It is the same fear-ridden reaction we see gripping Reaganite conservatives and the beneficiaries of other perceptual pogroms when it comes to any frame of mind that they have not included in the "official" scenario of reality. Any transcendental short-cuts or non-prescription vehicles toward "feeling-better" undermine

the reality-mediating role of the authorities. Rabelais wrote of
their fear in mythical terms:

"These strange exploits bred such astonishment to the celestial intelligences to all marine and celestial gods, that they were
on a sudden all afraid. From which amazement... they judged
it high time to call a council for their own safety and preservation. The Olympic gods, being all and each of them affrighted
at the sight of such achievements, said, Pantagruel hath... put
us more to a plunge and nearer our wit's end, by this sole herb
of his, then did of old the Aliodae by overturning mountains."

Rabelais even went so far as to speculate about the future
exploration of the kingdom of the mind, the "celestial sphere"
that might be unlocked by the discovery of other herbs with
new and unimagined properties:

"Who knows but by his (Pantagruel's) sons may be found out
an herb of such another virtue and prodigious energy, as that
by the aid thereof in using it aright according to their father's
skill, they may contrive a way for human kind to pierce into
the high aerian clouds, get up into the spring-head of the
hail, take an inspection of the snowy sources, and shut and
open as they please the sluices from whence proceed the
floodgates of the rain; then prosecuting their etherial voyage,
they may step into the lightning workhouse and shop, where
all the thunderbolts are forged, where, seizing on a magazine
of heaven, and storehouse of our warlike munition, they may
discharge a bouncing peal or two of thundering ordance, for
joy of their arrival to these new supernal places."

And Rabelais portrayed the gods in great distress at such
human boldness. He records for us their imagined lament:

"We shall not then be able to resist the impetuosity of their
intrusion, nor put a stoppage to their entering in at all,

whatever regions, domiciles, or mansions of the spangled firmament they shall have any mind to see, to stay in, or to travel through for their own recreation. There will be sojourners come from earth who, longing after the taste of sweet cream, of their own skimming off, from the best milk of the dairy of the galaxy, and take to their own beds at night for wives and concubines, our fairest goddesses, the only means whereby they can be deified."

There would certainly have been no sense in expounding on this enticing information unless Rabelais proceeded to instruct his inexperienced readers on how to use the magnificent herb. As it turns out, given the restrictions on clear exposition he had to impose on himself, he managed quite well, using an ingenious myth that he hoped would tempt the curious and the daring to discover for themselves the delights of Pantagruelion.

Chapter 52 of Book III relates the amazing fable concerning "How a certain kind of Pantagruelion is of that nature that the fire is not able to consume it." First, it is noteworthy that Rabelais suggests different varieties of the plant. Second, the statement that the plant will not burn is extraordinary enough to tempt experimentation with the plant in the presence of fire. Readers smitten by curiosity on this point were equally likely to be smitten, finally and pleasantly, by the singular virtues of the plant Rabelais called "Pantagruelion." A happy discovery that would also, upon re-reading the author's words, unlock their secret references and make their meaning plain.

"Arabians, Indians, Sabaens,
Sing not, in hymns or Io Paens,
Your incense, myrrh, or ebony.
Come here, a nobler plant to see,
And carry home, at any rate,

some seed, that you may propagate.
If in your soil it takes, to heaven
A thousand thousand thanks be given;
And say, with France it goodly goes,
Where the Pantagruelion grows."

—Rabelais

DISNEY'S INTRAPSYCHIC DRAMA *SNOW WHITE AND THE SEVEN DWARFS:* A GROFIAN INTERPRETATION

by Thomas B. Roberts, Ph.D.

One of the advantages of living in a university community is that the townspeople develop some tolerance for odd behavior—on the part of both students and their professors. Clipboard in hand, I was a beneficiary of this tolerance several years ago when I attended the Saturday matinee, Saturday evening show, and Sunday matinee of Disney's *Snow White and the Seven Dwarfs.* Sitting near the front so that I'd have enough light, I studiously scribbled notes while around me children and their parents divided their attention between the silver-screen adventures of the pubescent heroine and the pragmatic pitfalls of popcorn, gaining the attention of friends from school, spilled soft drinks, and going to the restroom alone and finding one's way back alone.

Seated in niches to the upper left and right of the stage,

two gold-painted statues of Rameses II, each 10 feet high, presided over twentieth century versions of the hero legend on the screen and rites of passage to middle childhood in the orchestra.

Built in 1929 in the wake of America's fascination with Egyptiana following the opening of King Tut's tomb seven years earlier, the Egyptian Theatre in DeKalb, Illinois, was not yet a historical landmark. Several toes of one pharaoh revealed that even God-king's may have feet of plaster. Part of a pyramid had sloughed off the right-hand wall, and overhead the formerly twinkling stars of the ancient Egyptian sky had all burned out their bulbs.

It was the weekend following Easter, and I had just returned from a professional annual pilgrimage. As they do each year during the post-Easter week, the Research Department of the Menninger Foundation holds a week-long conference at Council Grove, Kansas, a town named for Indian councils held there in pre-Santa Fe Trail days. "Council Grove," as the conference is known familiarly, intentionally publishes no proceedings and discourages coverage by both professional and public press. This is done in order to allow the participants a safe environment in which to try out and develop new ideas and speculations before they are ready to be published or presented at professional meetings. Early research in biofeedback, shamanistic healing, meditation, psychedelic drugs, imagery, Eastern philosophies, spiritual psychologies, and similar mind-body topics made their appearance at Council Grove several years before being presented to professional groups and the general public.

As is often the case at professional meetings, the informal get-togethers are as important as the formal presentations. One evening at dinner my companions mentioned that the seven dwarfs in *Snow White* are a fairy tale expression of this often mystical number. They said that in certain parts of Buddhism, Hinduism, Christianity, and in some esoteric Western psychologies the number seven carries special importance. Each dwarf, they said, was a personification of one of the seven chakras in Hinduism. When I arrived home Friday evening, I discovered by happy synchronicity that Disney's *Snow White and the Seven Dwarfs* had just started at the Egyptian Theatre. With chakras in mind and clipboard in hand, I chose a seat between the two pharaohs.

Synchronicity struck again. The next week my transpersonal education class was assigned *Realms of the Human Unconscious: Observations from LSD Research*[1] by Stanislav Grof. To my surprised delight Grof's model invested Disney's movie with meanings I had not expected. That week we discussed Grof's model in class, then made a graduate-student field trip to see the movie yet again. The Egyptian staff looked surprised to see a large group of adults appear for a midweek showing and then sit in a tight bunch together, intermittently whispering, smiling, and nodding knowingly to each other.

A Transpersonal History

In *Hero with a Thousand Faces*[2] Joseph Campbell says that although legends, folk tales, myths, and fairy tales are told as if they were stories of external events, happening to a hero or heroine in the real material world, fundamentally they are psychological stories of inner, intrapsychic events. According to this view, stories which persist over time do so because they carry universal psychological messages that activate the psyches of their readers, hearers, or viewers. Stories which appeal only to personal histories or particular times and places may be popular briefly, but their interest will wane as events in the real world change. Great literature, the world's major religions, folk tales, legends, and other persistent stories strum psychological chords that are deeper than one's personal experiences and more universal than the daily events of historical time and place.

Looked at in this way, *Snow White* is much more than a children's tale. Stretching across the centuries from a folk tale in an oral tradition through written forms and now a movie, *Snow White* offers a way to study human psychological processes. *Snow White* becomes a general case of psychological crisis and growth which represents common problems and their resolution. Parts of the psyche are represented by characters in the story, and internal psychological events are described as interactions between these characters. When we look at the Queen, the Peddler-Witch and Snow White, for example, we are seeing a dramatization of an intrapsychic struggle.

Although the connection between the dwarfs and the chakras initiated my psychocritical interest in Disney's version of *Snow White*, that interest was maintained by the excitement of recognizing other transpersonal elements in the movie: Jungian archetypes, Campbell's concept of the mythic hero's journey, the parallels between the standard introduction to fairy tales and the meaning of "transpersonal," and, most important, Grof's cartography of the human unconscious. Taken together, these ideas deepen and enrich our understandings of this movie and of other heroes' journeys.

The Seven Chakras

In Tibetan Buddhism, Hinduism, and some related religions, the chakras are understood as centers of psychospiritual development located within the human body. Although there are some variations in the chakra system from one sect to another, there is agreement on most of the basics. From a

Western viewpoint, which is more skeptical on spiritual matters, chakras might be considered hypothetical constructs; that is, useful ideas whose material reality is speculative.

Physiologically, each chakra is associated with a nexus of nerves, a location along the spine or head, and a gland or glands. Psychologically, each is associated with a value system, personality characteristics, and levels of psychological and spiritual development. Some religious and esoteric systems also associate them with colors, sounds, shapes, jewels, lotus flowers, and so on and on and on. The voluminous literature on chakras is elaborate, esoteric, and far beyond the scope of this article. For our purposes it is enough to note that they are seen as existing in a very deep part of the human mind or psyche, a level much deeper than most Western psychologists realize. The full development of a spiritually and psychologically healthy personality cannot take place unless each chakra is clean, active, and an open conduit for spiritual energy. In *Snow White* we will see our heroine working on this part of her unconscious after she enters the transpersonal level of her mind. Possible connections between the chakras and the dwarfs were the original stimulus for my seeing *Snow White*, but they are not the central thrust of this interpretation.

Jungian Archetypes

According to Jungian psychologists the persistence of certain folk tales and myths and their appearance among many cultures is due to the fact that they activate deep layers of the human mind that all people have in common. This layer of the mind is not a product of the experiences each person has during his or her lifetime. That is, it is not a personal layer of memories and experiences: it goes beyond the personal; it is transpersonal.

Among the items in this part of our minds are archetypes. These are inborn predispositions to react to our experiences in certain ways. They may be processes such as birth or death, roles such as earth-mother or wise old man, natural objects such as mountains or sunsets, or man-made objects such as rings and weapons.. Stories, tales, legends, myths, and even movies which include these items will provoke unconscious responses in us.

Among the prominent archetypes in Disney's *Snow White* are anima/animus and persona/shadow. the persona is the face we present to the world in order to be socially acceptable. The Queen-Stepmother shows this in her obsessive desire to be the "fairest one of all." Her shadow is that aspect of herself that contains the characteristics she most dislikes, ugliness, age, and decrepitude. Like that of most people, her shadow is violent and destructive and remains suppressed for most of the movie, but emerges as the Peddler-Witch.

In order to have a full and vigorous life, a person must tame the shadow's destructive impulses and use them in a constructive way. This process of integrating the persona and shadow is psychotherapeutic, and we watch some of it happening in *Snow White.*

The integration of the archetypes anima and animus is closely related to the persona-shadow integration and is also a necessary step to becoming a fully functioning person. We also see this happen in *Snow White*. The anima is the female side of the male psyche, and the animus is the male side of the human psyche. When these are suppressed rather than expressed, they form part of the shadow. In the Queen we see a suppressed anima coming forth destructively in her domination of the huntsman and instructions to him to kill Snow White, who characteristically represents the anima's stereotype—pretty, helpless, and weak. If we are to have a well-balanced person, the Queen, Peddler-Witch, and Snow White must become integrated.

Likewise, the animus is split and unbalanced. The Huntsman-Animus, in spite of his appearance as a muscular outdoorsman, is fearful, weak, and subservient to the Queen. He stands hat-in-hand before her as she sits on her powerful throne. The underdeveloped Prince-Animus needs to be integrated with the Huntsman. The archetype group of persona, shadow, anima, and animus need to orchestrate their characteristics into a harmonious whole.

Introduction/Induction

Is the "once-upon-a-time" beginning to many fairy tales and legends actually an induction to a special state of consciousness? Consciousness psychocriticism raises this question and presents some interesting points about it. Among the many meanings of "transpersonal," Grof proposes "experiences involving an expansion of extension of consciousness beyond the usual ego boundaries and beyond the usual limits of time and/or space." Ego, time, and space are the three limits which are surpassed by transpersonal experiences. These three elements also appear in the frequent once-upon-a-time introduction to myths, legends, and fairy tales. "Once upon a time" or its equivalent does not merely point to a specific date in the historical past. It tells us we are actually in a timeless, eternal present. "Once upon a time" is all time. Likewise, "in a far-off land" does not designate a specific longitude and latitude. It removes us from the real world to "The Land of Make-Believe," as it is sometimes called. Imaginary space-time is space-time created by psychological processes, not the processes of physical reality. "We aren't in Kansas anymore, Toto." These phrases and their counterparts take us to the mythopoetic world where the realities of our ordinary world may or may not take hold.

The third element in the introduction of psychomythic adventures is a change in personal identity. We are given a hero or heroine to identify with. "Transpersonal" includes going beyond personal identity. It does not mean interpersonal, social, or collective; these refer to groups of interrelated individuals and are at base still rooted to the idea of an individual person or identity. During transpersonal states, the boundaries of identity are transcended: personal identity expands to include more than what Alan Watts called "the skin-encapsulated ego."

In tales of the hero's journey we are invited to transfer our identity to the hero or heroine who lives in mythopoetic spacetime. Princes and princesses, common folk, children, orphans, Greek heroes, and various kinds of adventurers all serve this purpose well. After disidentifying with our personal selves, we can reidentify with the main character in mythopoetic space-time, who represents part of our unconscious.

When space, time, and identity can vary, anything can happen. It is interesting to note the parallel between transpersonal psychology and psychocriticism on the one hand and contemporary physics on the other. In both fields, time, space, and identity (the "objective" observer) become variables.

Does the introduction of *Snow White* or the beginning of any other legend (whether explicit or not) do more than let us know that the story has begun? Like a hypnotist's "you are getting sleepy," does "once-upon-a-time" actually help induce a mythopoetic state of consciousness? It's not hard to imagine our ancestors of several hundred years ago slipping easily into a receptive, free-floating imagery-filled state. Tired after a long day full of hours of hard labor, almost certainly malnourished (chemically unbalanced) by today's standards, then finally eating a meal and perhaps drinking beer or wine, they settle by a fire while staring at the flames, and the story teller intones, "Once upon a time a long time ago..." How easy it is to drink the mythopoetic cup!

Today we stare glassy-eyed at television, have a drink or a toke, put on headphones and "space out," or enter a darkened theater. Relaxations, focused attention, a chemical aid, and willing suspension of disbelief (the cognitive functions of our ordinary state of consciousness)—the recipe remains unchanged across the centuries.

Chakras, archetypes, the hero's journey, and mythopoetic induction are transpersonal counterpoints to the Grofian theme. Each of these ideas deserves to be developed more fully; but such developments are beyond the scope of this chapter.

Grof's Landmarks in Disney's Land

As the theater lights dim and our attention is focused on the screen, the opening shot of *Snow White* lets us know that we are in the psychological space-time of mythopoetic reality: "We're not in Kansas anymore, Toto." Although we are not told that we are in a far-off land, the camera's view of a fairyland castle on precipitous promontory lets us know this isn't Kansas.

Abstract and Aesthetic Level

Disney's movie, like Grof's theory, pays little attention to this stage, but in terms of the movie, we are introduced to many of the main characters and themes: While in terms of psychocriticism, we are introduced to parts of the personality that need to be developed and integrated. The process that accompanies this psychotherapeutic process is begun when the Queen-Persona begins to doubt the truth of her self-concept. In a classic image of self-examination, she observes herself in a mirror and asks whether she is the fairest one of all. Willingness to look at oneself is the opening key to psychotherapy and personal growth. As some therapist say, when a client is willing to examine himself or herself, much of the therapeutic process is already accomplished.

Prince Animus shows up astride his big white animus, appropriately outside the castle walls. Snow White is shown washing the castle steps. She is dejected and downcast while she works; significantly, later we will see her doing similar work with a different inner understanding. In a parallel scene to the persona looking into the mirror, the pubescent Anima looks down a well, a classic symbol of looking into the deep unconsciousness. As she gazes at her reflection in the bottom, she sings, "I'm dreaming that the one I love will find me some day," and she spots the Prince's reflection united with hers in the perfect circle at the bottom of the well.

This tells us the direction the story will take, but the various parts of the personality must mature and strengthen before this unity and psychological integration can take place. This first glimpse is overwhelming for her, so she runs into the castle, but she is intrigued enough to watch coyly out of a window. The Prince sings a love song, and blows her a kiss.

Unity Theme

As is appropriate for the love-story aspect of *Snow White*, a motif of love-unity/wholeness-oneness appears from time to time. Since most experiences, including images and symbols, are presumed to interact with many levels of the human mind simultaneously, they may carry multiple meanings. The unity theme exemplifies this. In addition to expressing the Anima-Animus romance, and overall psychological integration, this theme takes on additional meanings from the perspective of transpersonal psychocriticism. These are the twin ideas of the healthiest psychological integration and highest spiritual development. To many transpersonal psychotherapists and psychologists optimal mental health and optimal spiritual development are identical. Other transpersonal psychologists would not go so far as to assert their identity but would see them as closely connected.

When he first appears outside the castle walls, the Prince sings, "I have only one song, one love." And his motivation is echoed by Snow White when she sings down the well, "I'm dreaming of the one I love." Given the naive adolescence of the characters, they probably do not see the greater psychological and spiritual significance of their quest for wholeness. Although psychological integration forms an overall theme of the movie, it's unlikely that the average movie-goer, child or adult, sees this theme either. But motivation and meaning are often obscured. The unity theme is more than a love story; it is also an expression of the desire for the combined goal of psychological wholeness and spiritual oneness.

Dwelling Theme

A minor motif that begins here is the dwelling theme. A house or other building is often taken to represent either oneself or one's life. Although this may not be important in *Snow White*, this minor theme adds to the psychological story somewhat. In the exposition the castle is a turreted, fairy tale castle, similar to the castle in Disneyland's Magic Kingdom. As the Prince appears outside its walls, the castle appears to be more a medieval defensive castle. The Snow White (immature anima) part of the personality will forego this luxury for the humble dwarfs' cottage, while the Shadow-Queen appears later in a dark, foreboding, mist-enshrouded castle at night. Finally, at the very end of the movie, Snow White and the Prince move toward a golden, spiritual castle in the sky.

These introductory scenes also introduce us to birds and animals, which may represent psychic and intuitive abilities. It is common in myths, legends, and children's stories, especially in Disney movies, for animals to have a "sixth sense" about what to do and not to do, where to go and what to avoid, and so forth. They sometimes act as telepathic agents and clairvoyant messengers or symbolize psychic abilities. We will see this later in *Snow White* too.

By presenting parts of the psyche that will become integrated during the movie and by starting the psychotherapeutic adventure with the mirror and well, the opening scenes of *Snow White* start us on the heroine's journey. As Campbell says, ostensibly the journey is outward into the world, fundamentally it is an inner, psychological journey.

Personal History, The Freudian Level

In Grof's model the second layer is called the recollective or personal history level. As the location of both the conscious and unconscious experiences from one's life, it is the focus of almost all current Western psychotherapies. Most Western schools of psychocriticisms are also biographical schools. Memories at this level include both actual events and imagined experiences. Grof's theory departs from standard Freudian psychodynamic theory by postulating that memories are not grouped around complexes and developmental crises but grouped according to emotions. For example, memories of guilt, anger, or fear would each form a cluster of associated memories. These clumps, called COEXs, "are constellations of memories consisting of condensed experiences (and related fantasies) from different life periods of the individual. The memories belonging to a particular COEX system have a similar basic theme or contain similar elements and are associated with a strong emotional charge of the same quality."[3] (p. 46)

In *Snow White* the brief Freudian-level scenes can be thought of as either Electral or Laiusian in nature. The Electra complex suggests the daughter's desire for the father (perhaps symbolized here by the Prince) and her resulting fears of the mother. In the Laius complex the father usually shows jealousy for the youth and vigor of the son; in *Snow White* we have a female version of this in the Queen's jealousy for the Prince's attention to Snow White and for her beauty. She then instructs the Huntsman to kill Snow White and bring her heart back in a box.

Perinatal Adventures

The special contributions of Grofian criticism exist in the movie's perinatal and transpersonal sequences. In *Snow White* the four perinatal stages appear in order for the heroine, and partially recur for the Shadow-Witch-Peddler. The perinatal level consists of four "basic perinatal matrices," or BPMs as they are called. Each BPM contains certain characteristic emotions, symbols, and themes. Like the COEXs on the personal-history level, the BPMs organize experiences and memories on the perinatal level. We see these themes occur in the same order as birth in *Snow White*, although they may not be so organized during actual psychotherapy.

Oceanic Bliss

The first BPM takes its overall theme from undisturbed intrauterine existence. This may show in memories and fantasies such as happy moments from childhood, or vacations in beautiful natural surroundings. The feeling is one of peaceful rest. In *Snow White* we see this when the Huntsman takes Snow White to a sunny glade in the woods. He remains at a distance in the background. While there she picks flowers, sings, and finds a fledgling, which she puts back in its nest. She is a fledgling out of her nest too, but does not know this yet. In a nice bit of movie-making the camera widens its angle by zooming back, and the sunny glade appears surrounded by a threatening, dark woods.

No-exit Hell

BPM II is characterized by antagonism with the mother during birth and is activated and symbolized by situations that endanger survival and bodily integrity, which could hardly be more intensive than having one's heart cut out. Other common BPM II themes are rejection (which is certainly Snow White's predicament) and unbearable and inescapable situations.

With her back against a boulder and with the huge Huntsman bearing down on her with dagger raised, Snow White is in the typical BPM II situation, between a rock and hard place. But the cowardly Huntsman-Animus cannot go through with the murder, and cries to Snow White to run away. She flees into the BPM III forest.

Titanic Struggle

"Struggles, frights, adventurous activities...intensification of suffering to cosmic dimensions...wild adventures, and dangerous explorations..."[4] (pp. 102–103), Snow White's panic-stricken flight through the dark forest has all of these BPM III elements. Disney the artist was often at his psychological best in such scenes. The woods become darker and darker. The branches grasp Snow White as she flies by. Evil-looking eyes follow her wherever she goes, and loom before her wherever she turns. Tree branches turn into dangerous talons, and the space around her threatens to close in on her.

Another aspect of BPM III is a scatological theme. Urine, feces, mucus, blood, and other repulsive substances occur in symbolic form when this part of the unconscious is engaged. Snow White trip and falls down a large hole into a sewer-like underground river. Tree stumps turn into alligator-like jaws and threaten to crush her, but unlike the situation in BPM II, she is not the helpless trapped victim. She can struggle, and does. The ferocious eyes become larger and more menacing. Finally, she trips over a large tree root and falls. The screen goes black.

Death-Rebirth

A major BPM theme running through the perinatal level is the death-rebirth theme. This sequence begins in BPM II with feelings of being hopelessly trapped in death and decay. It moves from endless torture of BPM II to the energetic struggle in BPM III, where it is resolved by a death-rebirth experience and progression into BPM IV's fresh, new day.

Grof's description of imagery typically associated with BPM II describes the onset of Snow White's run through the woods: "...black and dangerous-looking caverns; treacherous swamps; the beginning of tempests and ocean storms, with increasing atmospheric tension and darkening of the sky..."[5] (p. 144).

The hopelessness of BPM II becomes the furor of BPM III in Snow White's flight through the woods. It resolves itself in BPM III death and BPM IV rebirth. In the movie we see Snow White give up her struggle and apparently die as the screen goes black. The original 1937 Disney book version of *Snow White*, which coincided with the movie's first release, is more specific: "She stumble over a big root and fell. There was a roaring in her ears; she still seemed to hear the huntsman crying, 'Go! Go! Go!' But she could go not further. She was so miserable that she didn't care what happened. She wanted to lie there and die."

From Grof's perspective the death-rebirth experience "represents the termination and resolution of the death-rebirth struggle. Suffering and agony culminate in an experience of total annihilation...This experience is usually referred to as *ego death*."[6] (pp. 138–139)

In Grof's theory the death-rebirth experience is a major crisis and opportunity for psychological growth. It can be the death of a narrower self and the birth of a wider, more mature self. It allows a person to gain a wider perspective on his or her life by ending childish emotional and cognitive attachments, including attachment to one's self. After the death-rebirth experience the person becomes less egotistical and more dedicated to love and service. Snow White goes through this transformation as she moves into BPM IV.

Dawning of a New Day

The transition from BPM III to BPM IV portrays the crisis and breakdown of a weaker personality organization and its replacement by a stronger organization. To someone going through this process, one's situation in life has changed. We see this in *Snow White*. As she falls into the blackness of ego despair and ego death, the ferocious eyes in the nighttime forest glare at her. After her rebirth a moment later, the same eyes transform into the cute, cuddly eyes of the Disney forest creatures. Squirrels, raccoons, bunnies, and birds replace the monsters of BPM III; rather they are *seen* in a new psychological light. What was terrifying at one minute becomes friendly and inviting the next. As dawn arrives, the claustrophobigenic and threatening forest shapes of the night become the everyday trees of the forest.

In LSD sessions, BPM IV often is expressed in memories, fantasies and images of expansiveness, beautiful colors, sensory enhancement, appreciation of a simple way of life, and natural scenes such as sunrise. Several themes appear in the BPM IV sequence of scenes. In addition to the death-rebirth theme, we see that Snow White is somewhat more integrated psychologically, although she still has a long way to go. She asks the birds and animals, her psychic and intuitive abilities, where to go, and they direct her to the dwarf's cottage— appreciation of a humble way of life. For the first time a visual theme appears, one which reappears frequently in the background of the movie from this point on, but one which plays no direct role in the plot.

Shrooms Galore

In the forest glade where Snow White awakens, at the base of trees in the background, are red-capped mushrooms with small white dots on their caps. Thus begins the fungi-festooned-forest-floor leitmotif. From here on in the movie, Amanitas will appear regularly. According to Schultes, world authority on psychoactive plants, the effects of Amanita include: "...a feeling of ease characterized by happiness, a desire to sing and dance, colored visions...Participants are sometimes overtaken by curious beliefs, such as that experienced by an ancient tribesman who insisted that he had just been born! Religious fervor often accompanies the inebriation."[7] (pp. 25–26)

Rumors aside, this is not proof that Disney actually consumed Amanitas or other SOC-changing plants. He may have chosen the beauties for their aesthetic value, just as their popularity in the design of domestic and children's objects is probably more for their color than their psychoactive properties. Perhaps the appearance of mushrooms, cacti, and morning glories in the opening sequence of *Fantasia* is chance too. There are non-drug ways of getting in touch with these parts of one's unconscious, and psychologically aware artists would be expected to perceive and portray their inner voyages.

Beyond the Self—Transpersonal Adventures

Led by her psychic and intuitive abilities, Snow White spots the dwarfs' humble cottage across a small stream. When she crosses this Rubicon, she'll be in Transpersonaland. The cleaning and cooking she does there contains both some unresolved BPM III elements and transpersonal elements.

She sees that the cottage—her psychological self—is a mess, and unlike her previous distaste for cleaning at the castle steps, she now charges right into the dirt and dust with manic activity: "Whistle while you work." Working on oneself (cleaning up one's act) is frequently a way difficult psychotherapy is symbolized. As Grof points out, manic activity and wanting to throw a party (the dwarfs' dinner) is typical of BPM IV if there are still unresolved issues from BPM III; as we will see later in the dungeon sequence, the Persona and Shadow still need to be integrated. At this point little Anima has matured considerably and is taking responsibility for her own actions and goals and is even directing the actions of others, her animal and bird helpers.

In terms of her inner journey we have seen Snow White glance down the well into her subconscious, pass through a brief Freudian stage of conflict with her mother-substitute, move through the entire perinatal sequence, and start her transpersonal development. Now she must go still deeper into her mind. After cleaning the house and preparing dinner, she goes upstairs to put herself into a still deeper state of consciousness. When she "awakens" from her "sleep," she will discover the seven chakras.

The Seven Chakras

Meanwhile deep within the mind mine, the chakra-dwarfs are busily digging. They aren't mining coal, or iron, or any other metal. They are mining jewels, and in Eastern and esoteric traditions a jewel is located at the center of each chakra. Alternately, a jewel is sometimes pictured at the crown chakra at the top of the head, representing a connection between the worldly state of man and matter and the higher state of spirit and enlightenment. Singing "Heigh-ho, heigh-ho, it's home from work we go," they march home through the fungal carpeted forest.

After some cinematic funny business when the dwarfs and Snow White discover each other, they start mutual nurturing and growth. Like a den of Cub Scouts coming in after school, they attack the heavily laden table. "Not until you've washed your faces and hands," Snow White says. She knows chakras must be clean as well as nourished. In spite of this outrageous request, they comply by washing at the watering trough...all except Grumpy. And there is more cinematic playfulness around the pump while getting Grumpy washed. After dinner the dwarfs teach Snow White a yodel song (mantra?) and dance (mudra?)[8] The following morning the dwarfs heigh-ho off to work, and Snow White picks up her mania for work by baking each of them a pie.

From Persona to Shadow

Meanwhile back at the castle, Queen Persona has decided to do a bit more self-reflecting and finds her rival is alive and living with the dwarfs. Her anger sends her down into the dungeon of her mind, where she concocts two potions. While preparing the first portion, she holds the glass chalice up to a window, and a bolt of lightning strikes it, electronizing the solution. In the language of psychedelia, "electric" is often used to characterize the most intense psychedelic experiences; for example, Tom Wolfe's book *The Electric Kool-Aid Acid Test.*[9] Disney's *Snow White*, of course, was produced long before the psychedelic Sixties, so Disney's use of this image did not come from this source.

The first portion is a Peddler's disguise, which she drinks, sending her on a prototypical "bad trip." She gasps for breath. Her own hand clutches at her throat and her eyes bulge wide with terror as she is caught in a vortex with no escape—typical BPM II.

Ordinarily, when one thinks of a disguise such things as changes in clothing, grooming, movement, and voice naturally come to mind. But drinking a disguise? That's an odd idea. Can one change one's appearance by drinking a chemical? Anthropological readings do contain instances of changes of identity resulting from ingesting and inhaling psychoactive substances. Where did Disney get his idea? Was he a student of shamanism? The transformation we are seeing is inner, psychological change. The beautiful, young, powerful, haughty vain Queen is expressing everything she wants least to be, an ugly, old, lowly crone. She has become her shadow. The second potion is intended for Snow White. It won't kill her, but will send her into a deep sleep (yet a still deeper SOC), which can be ended only by Love's First Kiss.

Snow White has continued on with her manic domestic chores, and her dedication to the service of others indicates she is spiritually more advanced than she was as the simple Anima washing the castle steps. When the Shadow-Peddler appears, she is immediately frightened, and her bird and animal intuitive and psychic abilities try to drive the old hag away. The peddler feigns sickness, and compassionate Snow White brings her into the cottage to recover. In false thankfulness, the Shadow gives Snow White the potion-dipped apple, telling her, "You will see the one you love." Personal attachments such as wealth, influence, or power do not tempt Snow White now that she is motivated by transpersonal values, but she still longs for integration with the Animus, for unity and cosmic oneness. She bites the apple, and is off to a still deeper realm of the hero's inner journey.

Meanwhile back at the mine, the dwarf's are digging their jewels. At least they are trying to, but Snow White's bird and animal familiars are pestering them by pulling at their beards and tugging at their clothes. The dwarfs think the birds and animals have gone batty. Sleepy, however, yawns and wonders aloud whether something is the matter with Snow White. They all immediately sense that this is the reason for the birds' and animals' odd behavior, and off they ride on animalback to rescue her, led by Grumpy.

It may be noteworthy that Sleepy recognizes the message of danger and that Grumpy leads the dwarf cavalry to the rescue. Sleepy, the sixth link of the chakra system, is located at the "third eye," a spot in the lower part of the forehead just above the eyebrows. This center is associated with telepathy, clairvoyance, and other psychic activities, so it is appropriate that Sleepy understands the message of danger at a distance. Sleepy has become more awake. Grumpy, who is located at the adrenals in the chakra system, represents both anger and excitement—adrenaline—he now is able to use his aggression appropriately. Doc, who stumbled over his words when he first met Snow White, now also speaks more clearly. Apparently, with Snow White's cleaning and nourishment the chakras are functioning better, although not perfectly.

The dwarfs chase the Peddler-Shadow up a steep cliff, and she is about to lever a huge boulder down on them, when (in good Campbellian fashion) they are rescued from beyond. A bolt of lightning breaks off the ledge where she is standing, and the last we see of the Peddler-Shadow, two vultures are circling. The dwarfs place Snow White in a glass casket in the woods. Together with all her feathered and fairy friends they weep at her loss.

Exeunt Omnes

Where are we now in the intrapsychic drama? The Persona and Shadow have been united and obliterated. The Huntsman part of the Animus is forgotten, and the Prince Animus is presumed to be out doing whatever Princes and their horses do in the woods. Little Anima has matured and gown stronger through a series of psychological adventures and now is in such a deep state of consciousness that she appears dead. The intuitive and psychic abilities and the chakras are all quietly mourning.

Suddenly, who should arrive astride his great white animus? "Some day my prince will come." The antidote for the potion is Love's First Kiss. He kisses her...nothing happens. She just lies there. Is something wrong? Then she stirs and awakens. Animus and Anima are united. To the jubilation of the dwarfs, birds, and animals, they ride off together toward the great spiritual castle in the golden clouds.

Notes

[1]Grof, Stanislav. *Realms of the Human Unconscious: Observations from LSD Research.* New York: E. P. Dutton, 1975.

[2]Campbell, Joseph. *The Hero with a Thousand Faces* (Bollingen Series) Princeton, N.J.: Princeton University Press, 1949.

[3]Grof, p. 46.

[4]Grof, pp. 102-103.

[5]Grof, p. 144.

[6]Grof, pp. 138-139.

[7]Schultes, Richard Evans. *Hallucinogenic Plants.* New York: Golden Press, 1976.

[8]In Eastern religions mantra is the use of a sound as an aid in spiritual development, mudra the use of a movement or posture.

[9]Wolfe, Tom. *The Electric Kool-Aid Acid Test.* New York: Farrar, Strauss and Giroux, 1968.

Bibliography

Bishop, Peter *Archetypal Topology* (1981) *Spring;* Spring Pub., Zurich.

Cott, Jonathan *Notes on Fairy Faith and the Ideas of Childhood in Beyond the Looking Glass* (1973) Stonehill Pub., N.Y.,

Graves, Robert *The White Goddess* (1948) McGraw-Hill, N.Y. Graves speaks of the "German folk-story *Snow White*" on p. 348.

Grof, Stanislav *Realms of the Human Unconscious: Observations From LSD Research* (1976) E.P. Dutton, N.Y.

Grof, Stanislav (with J. Halifax) *The Human Encounter with Death* (1977) E.P. Dutton, N.Y.

Grof, Stanislav *LSD Psychotherapy* (1980) Hunter House, Pomona, California.

Hillman, James *Anima II* (1974) *Spring*; Spring Publ, Zurich.

Hillman, James *An Inquiry into Image* (1977) *Spring*; Spring Pub., Zurich.

Jung, C. G. *Four Archetypes* (1973) Bollingen, Princeton The chapter *The Phenomenology of the Spirit in Fairytales* is especially relevant.

Jung, C. G. *The Spirit in Man, Art and Literature* (1966) Bollingen, Princeton.

Jung. C. G. *The Vision Seminars* (1976) Spring Publications, Zurich. Several excellent accounts of fairy tale symbology.

Pascal, Jeremy *Fifty Years of the Movies* (1981) Hamlyn Pub. Group, N.Y.

Stanford, Barbara *Myths and Modern Man* (1972) Wash. Square Press, N.Y.

Warshow, Robert *The Immediate Experience: Movies, Comics, Theatre and Other Aspects of Popular Culture* (1964) Doubleday/Anchor, N.Y.

Wilner, Harry A. *Epic Dreams and Heroic Ego* (1977) *Spring;* Spring Pub., Zurich.

MIKE'S STORY

by Phoenix Research Foundation

Introduction

Psychedelics empower healing. Many cultures have known this, some for millennia, and have explained it from many viewpoints more productive and more positive than the Western medical suggestion that LSD mimics psychosis (the "psychotomimetic" model). Mythology, for example, tells of archetypes such as the Phoenix and energies such as prana and Kundalini that are causal to healing and that operate at transpersonal levels of mind and reality. You may recall that the Phoenix is reputed to be immortal, and that when it consumes itself in flames, they burn away the detritus of its life and it emerges reborn and radiant. Are Phoenix and flame archetypes of eternal causal processes that can heal, purify and transform us? If so, can psychedelics help us invoke those, to mediate levels of healing and personal change that science has not yet reached?

To suggest that this is possible, here is a story about two psychedelic healing experiences. We describe these as occurring between us and Mike, a Viet Nam vet who was seeking to heal deep life issues including war trauma that innumerable veterans suffer from. We tell this story in the "first person" as occurring between us and Mike to protect the privacy of the parties while fairly describing what is possible.

We can all heal ourselves at various levels by dissolving negative patterns from earlier in our lives. We can all experience growth and psychospiritual transformation by strengthening positive patterns. We can all heal and grow at levels beyond those we already know. To describe these abilities, here is "Mike's Story."

The Story

Mike had always had problems. Perhaps they began before his birth, with shock to his mother when she was told his father had just died in an accident at work. Certainly they worsened as he was repeatedly abandoned and betrayed in childhood. To leave that behind, he volunteered for Viet Nam. After ten months of combat, a traitor tipped off the Viet Cong to his Company's landing zone and he and his buddies were hit with a three day firefight. When their ammunition ran out, it was bare hands, kill or be killed. Mike was a survivor—there weren't many.

Home at last. The therapist for his combat trauma said he was cured, but for twenty years he kept waking in a cold sweat as he relived that incident in his recurrent nightmare.

Marriage. He delivered their first child, stillborn, its umbilical cord wrapped three times around its neck. His wife blamed him. One day he walked in the front door and she emptied a magazine-fed .22 rifle at him. With his combat reflexes he slammed the rifle away and pinned her to the wall by her throat before he knew what was happening. Bullet holes through his coat; none through him.

Then he felt sick, knowing he was damned whatever he did. He put his wife out, closed the door, closed his heart, and started over.

He knew several crafts. Getting jobs was easy; getting fired was too, as his issues arose. A year here, two years there. No money, no peace, no trust. Learning to heal others, but a wounded healer, moving around, finally living out of his car. Failure scripts and continuing agony.

Within hours of meeting us, twenty years after Viet Nam, he had told us his story. He talked about his joy as a healer, and his pain as that career crashed several times. Loving music, he extemporized songs for us on his guitar. He had much to share and teach us. But dark undertones emerged. Repeated betrayals formed his life pattern. Danger. He said he was delighted to be visiting overnight, to become friends. Then he casually said "Don't startle me in the morning." Meaning "I'm dangerous. I trust only my reflexes. Who knows who's out to kill me?" Fantasy or fact—why these messages?

That night he slept in the guest room, and we tossed and turned in the room above him. After two hours I was on my fourth nightmare. Dara was dreaming of bare-handedly ripping a woman's heart out. She awoke choking, coughing, unable to breathe. The next day when we told Mike about this, he told us that in his fear and frenzy in Viet Nam he had pulled a man's heart out and brandished it at the enemy, screaming. Dara had tuned into this incident, his recurrent nightmare, in her sleep.

Later we discussed our life visions. We had never faced issues like Mike's, but we offered to try to guide him if he wished to take a leap of courage and use our one remaining evening together to reopen all his issues and see if he could overcome them with us. His parents. His foster home and childhood rejection. Viet Nam. His marriage and stillborn son. His failure scripts. His ego and money issues. We suspected that underlying all of these, he had a core need to feel the universe is safe despite the repeated assaults on his physical and emotional survival.

In our then-confrontive style, we told Mike to consider whether or not he felt safe with us, and whether he really wanted to go to his core and empty out. We warned him we would push him if he got stuck. He stayed in this pressure cooker a few hours, and then said "let's go for it."

At his request we gathered candles, wine, and his guitar, Wiccan staff and Athane (sacred dagger). He wove a song to the four directions, and cast a circle as a safe and sacred space. He invoked the God and Goddess to manifest themselves through him, to teach and bless him and us. He took an MDMA-class sacrament, which he had brought, to amplify his awareness. We, deeply privileged to witness normally secret rites, dedicated ourselves to be of service.

He struggled to ask for even simple things. How could he imagine others touching and loving him? We mirrored his struggle back to him, so he could see pathways he could develop to gain love and learn to tolerate rejection, which often comes to us all when others are afraid or unable to respond comfortably to us. To help him go past his limit in these areas, we held him like a baby. We hoped this would rebirth him in love. It intensified his fears, but the intensity and safety enabled him to see those fears and find a way through them.

After a time he needed to move to transform, and we tumbled about with him like a pile of puppies. With that he tapped into his deep kinesthetic sense of what he lost when his earlier relationships had ended. Above all, for him, the safety and acceptance. He became very emotional, and declared his deep need and desire to find another family.

He crafted and sang a long heart-felt verse in thanks for the insight. We thanked him for the gift of his song, but then we told him that he had retreated to his safe space—as though performing on stage, where rejection would be impersonal and true intimacy impossible. We asked him to express his emotions directly rather than filtering them through rhyme and rhythm.

He protested until he saw our unanimity. Then he tried, and soon he opened very deep emotions. Then he demanded his guitar and sang again, less defensively. A nice step forward. But he still used "third person" words—another defense, denying self, diminishing the power of his song and verse. When we said, "make it 'I', not Mankind," he crumbled completely, sobbing dry sobs, and choking—but did not consciously hear us. To speak from his 'I' would propel him into his full power as Bard and Man, which he feared; we had found his crossroad. When he stopped shaking, we said it again, He tried, and each time he forgot 'I', we gently reminded him. In the second stanza his voice filled out and mellowed with deeper inner resonance and authority, filling the room and our hearts.

He said he had shifted from first person to third person in his spiritual quest, on another's advice, to dissolve his ego. Beth said he must first strengthen and complete his ego before it would be right to dissolve it. He had trouble accepting this, and indeed would experiment further with both paths. But the change was begun.

Then he talked about his ex-wife and stillborn son. For an hour and a half, using psychodrama, the three of us played his son's spirit and his wife, and coached him when he got stuck. This enabled him to vividly relive his past and release the anger, frustration, guilt, sorrow and helplessness he still felt about both of them and his lost relationships. He realized that he and his wife both had been unable to express and share their grief. To release the past's dead hands and build new learning for the future, he acted out that sharing with us. Then he was finally able to end his grief by totally forgiving himself and his ex-wife from his heart.

Waves of pain arose in his abdomen as he released the agony he had unconsciously held in his gut. We told him to "loosen" around it as he would if it were a hot coal, and we gave him deep massage. He fought mightily to restrain his emotions, fearing that he might become violent, out of control, once again. We held him gently as he sobbed, cried and growled. His voice was weak and strangled, trapped within his throat. Finally it rose to a full scream, a howl of primal release and then of lusty rebirth.

Peace. After a few moments he began seeing positive things in his past that his anger had concealed. Then he sang and played Taps, to integrate this final farewell to his son and ex-wife and release any negative patterns he still held from that era.

Next he improvised a spiritual, mostly in the first person. It led him back again to his beginning, and forward through his issues of betrayal, from birth, childhood abandonment by his parents and others, then Viet Nam, his marriage, his healthcare schooling, and his career. He had felt repeatedly helpless, in uncontrollable and deeply wrong situations. He had felt unsafe all his life. He felt unendingly raped. This was what had held his gut. Beth continued deep massage, as he burped, strangled, and violently pounded and howled to release this hidden anguish.

Then he could put his actions in a larger perspective, and find honor in what he had done to survive. He saw, though, that his fear had brought further betrayal to him, time after time, and that he would have to build a new worldview and self-concept free from fear of betrayal in new experiences.

Relating his life to his spiritual beliefs, we suggested that his innate healing powers and empathy had been strengthened through his having experienced his woundings and healing. He had taken life and saved life many times, in a balanced whole. His God and Goddess had enacted their power of creation and destruction through him as a proper expression of the universe unfolding. (You may recognize themes from Shamanism, Wicca and the Bhagavad Gita.) We said that penance was not necessary, but was done, for acts necessary in the moment for his survival and to save other lives. We watched his micromuscle movements, skin tone and other physiology to see which of these "reframes" he unconsciously accepted and integrated, to be sure his changes would be permanent.

Then we showered, washing down the drain all the negativity that had come up, been sweated out, and released. This enlarged our mutual acceptance and safe space even further, showing he could safely expose his dark side. Then, since he had learned the power of forgiveness, he practiced forgiving himself and everyone else he could think of, regardless of whether he felt he had wronged them or they had wronged him, as we represented the others in turn.

Finally we showed him how and why to use affirmations and metaphors. We discussed the metaphors he naturally spoke in, and suggested more positive, open and balanced ones, like "completing" chapters of his life instead of "closing the books."

After that long evening we all slept well. Mike dreamt of butterflies.

Assimilation

Before Mike left, we took him aback by urging him to get into an intimate relationship. He thought his transformation was complete, but we knew that now he had become able to see his issues, and they would arise again for him to dissolve them. This is an aspect of how life teaches us all, and a part of his training to help others.

When we parted, he gave us his Wiccan staff to keep in our home as a continuing connection. He hadn't let anyone touch it until then. We kept our friendship active by phone for the next two years. He'll tell the rest in his words.

"Back home I felt like a stranger. Friends said I'd changed a lot, but they couldn't put words to it. A week or two later I went to a Pagan festival, as festival Bard. I reached altered consciousness and played out of my mind for about 40 minutes. I merged into my patron Pan and touched His essence while I was playing the Pan Pipes.

"There I met Evelyn. Soon we moved in together. Over the next year and a half, we had happier times than I'd been able to have before, but I hurt terribly whenever I fell back into old habits.

Perhaps I gave up too much of myself in trying to meet her needs. My life and my integrity slipped away almost without my awareness, and I fell back into irritation, depression and fear. I failed at my healthcare practice, and I knew that I would have to open my heart further to serve patients well. I took a demeaning job rather than be unemployed, but I resented that work and did it poorly. When I left it, Evelyn and I argued stormily and intensified our passive/aggressive battles. By the time I got a better job, I had replayed far too many of my earlier mistakes. This time, though, I was learning from them. I felt ready to choose a partner better suited to me, and knew I was able to relate from a positive core of integrity.

"I left my relationship with Evelyn on the coldest day in February. After I moped awhile, I found a place of my own and began to get my act together and seriously work on the issues I had most avoided: Self-honesty. dealing positively with others, meditating, even exercising, I hate to exercise. I have Master level skills—third degree black belt in Shokunryu Karate, and more, that I developed here and in Nam. But my skills have no soul without opening my love and letting go of what I know in order to learn anew. I did that with Phoenix, and had to do it now to rebuild my life.

"I saw how much my relationships had been ego—I want, I want—not what I truly need or what I can give. Still, there was much good. My hours as Pan: Gods don't come to fools. Seeking the deeper mysteries in life, as Bard and Priest. Opening the heart level with Phoenix; building my ability to keep my heart open, and knowing that is a gateway to the mysteries.

Integration

"The Fall after I left Evelyn I was ready to visit Phoenix again. When I arrived, for two days they told me, step by step, about levels of consciousness that I might reach if I were ready and if they could mediate an energy field for direct induction. I believed two levels they described, heart level and seeing archetypes, since I had known heart level and had seen Pan. But the other levels seemed beyond possibility; I struggled to even suspend my disbelief.

"On the third morning Martin and I began a rite, alone. I created sacred space in the Wiccan manner, they being eager that I trust my framework rather than try theirs. I cast the Circle, called the quarters and invoked the presence of the Lady. We shared a major sacrament (such as LSD, psilocybin or mescaline). Then we waited for our consciousness to rise to transformative levels.

"As the atmosphere became more sacred, I cast the Tarot. My theme card was the Queen of Cups—royalty, receptivity and relationship. My issue card was the Devil: my negativity, false perceptions and unwillingness to look at my own issues stared at me. Then Queens, the Hierophant, the Lovers, high cards signifying relationship and the Lady and the Mysteries I have been seeking all of my life. Then the Ace of Rods, with deep meaning for both of us. Finally the Magician, powerful and clear. I had never cast such a spread. Then Martin cast a spread, and its power and the way it mirrored mine, utterly blew me away.

"I invoked my theme card to open heart space by visualizing that I was a Chalice filling with love. My heart opened like a lotus, and I joyously recognized 'Yes, this is what I'm supposed to be doing. This is right! And Holy!' I felt love, acceptance and bliss flow into me, replacing fear and anger. My breathing deepened and the air felt alive. My vision cleared, and I saw perfection around and within me. I sensed divinity even in those who had wronged me, and felt able to give and receive nurturing instead of having to send defensive messages that everyone should fear me. I became grateful for my survival and hopeful for my future.

"From time to time Martin looked into my eyes to calibrate the rising energy. He still sensed that I had a deeper wall I didn't know of and didn't know how to get through. He saw a block, as a steel gate at my cornea. Staying totally calm and relaxed, he just waited and willed this to shift. Gradually I realized our eye contact was cutting away more and more inner resistance. I felt my energy increasing and running through me. Limits dropped away. Residual fear?...partially. Issues?...certainly. I wasn't aware of all their content, yet I could feel myself clearing at level after level as we sat eye to eye and the energy kept rising. I began to have an incredible sense of relief, empowerment and excitement.

"Suddenly between one breath and the next we went higher. As I came into sync with Martin, I became aware of his aura, and its color shifts, and then the colors and forms of the energy running between us.

"Then...on Martin's face and at times on his body I saw Zeus, head of the Greek Gods, then my patron Pan. Martin saw the Hindu divinity Ganesha, son of Shiva and Parvati, bringer of happiness and wealth. Then I saw images of Christ and Mary. Then twice a Tibetan Doré devil mask. This gave way to Pan again, then the Lady. Finally a Norse archetype: Thor the Thunderer, or Balder the guardian of the rainbow bridge. We were SEEING archetypes!

"Zeus and Pan and Ganesha confirmed that we had reached a sacred level. The Doré's bright red lips, over-large teeth, and wide and very round eyes mirrored the Devil I had cast at Tarot; Tarot and archetypes agreed I must unmask myself and face my issues. For that, Martin told me to face and merge into this mask, to become it for the moment. When I did, I felt immense positive energy, theretofore hidden from me by my bedeviling fears, release and dissolve personal blocks as though my energy and harmony were changing. That balanced my male and female energies and returned me to Pan and the Lady. Finally, Thor and/or Balder—the right hand being hidden I couldn't tell which—told me that I had intermixed power and spirituality in ways that I had to work through next.

"But first we danced to integrate the changes I had just made. I saw Martin as Shiva dancing. I felt Pan inhabit me again, and, playing my imaginary Pan pipes, I saw our energy flowing and interweaving in a double helix that spiralled and expanded to fill the room as we intermingled our energy bodies visually and psychically. Finally we stopped for food and a break.

"Then, facing each other, we lost our sense of separateness. Our minds overlapped and fused. I was scared, then exhilarated. I expanded, became everything, blended, merged, became whole myself and yet merged with another person and cared for me / we / life more deeply than language can convey. this must be IT!

"After some moments Martin took us even higher. A subtle energy of vast intelligence entered us to transform us further. As we entered each other's minds through our eyes, my issues and blocks appeared as a content-free fog between us. It dissipated as I released them. Then, as the archetypal imagery of Christ and Mary had foretold, my issue about Christianity arose. Could I heal even that? I had begun Seminary to become a priest, but was thrown out for asking too many questions. Now I realized as my truth that all Gods are One and all Goddesses are One and God and Goddess are One. For the first time I comprehended that we can all serve Christian or other aspects of the One, and yet all serve the One.

"I thought Martin could not know my thoughts, as we did this energy work without discussing its content. Martin said we should dance again to integrate the changes he saw. Jewish though he is, he unerringly picked the gospel album Ocean. I started to object, but stopped when I remembered that I had agreed to be receptive and face my issues. So we danced to 'Put Your Hand in the Hand', and I even sang its words in my Bardic voice. That did it; I let go of my issue and was healed.

"I knew that now I needed to be in water. We got in the shower, and soon it became a combination baptism, initiation and rebirthing. I felt my throat tense and close, and had the fear that I first knew when I had stopped breathing for about a minute during my birth. As I fought to breathe now, Martin sensed that I was reliving birth trauma, and rubbed my chest with his soapy hand to let physical pressure and the energy he ran from his hand help me open and relax my breathing. It seemed that subtle membranes began parting as the pressure and energy did its work. Then I began breathing deeply, drawing and expelling much more air than ever before. I saw a candle flame in the middle of space, at first as though through gauzy curtains, then like the heart of a sun. I became the flame, and then I saw the space between the stars.

"Martin encouragingly said 'I thought I would have to work at this. You're doing all the work.' I felt I had to sing. When Martin heard all was well, he left me singing in the shower, and my song came up from my gut and then it came out as my call.

"I didn't have control of my new voice yet. That made me feel frustrated and a little afraid. When I realized the hard part was done, this passed, and my call came out as a tone and then modulated into the "hear me" pattern. Each time it was stronger, fuller, more vibrant. I could hear its echoes, not just in the shower but in my voice itself. WOW! I poured every bit of my new power into it, the way I had tried to play my music but couldn't. It was beautiful. I didn't recognize my voice. This wasn't me. Who? WHAT? What was going on here?

"Feeling as weak as a baby, I rested awhile. Then we sat face to face and raised the energy again. I saw the nerve pathways and synapses in my brain, with energy running in red, yellow, blue and gold. 'That's neat, I haven't seen that since neuroanatomy', I thought.

"Martin opened himself totally, to the reimprinting level, and asked me to tune into his energy field and match it. We became very still and aware. A thick layered San Francisco fog arose. He said 'This is your holding the Nam thing; let it ALL go now. Let it ALL go.' And I let go of the rest of my Nam trauma. That was my last barrier; I opened up all the way, completely. I vaguely heard Martin telling me to stay open to the imprint. With all my effort I stayed open, as he softly said things I didn't even try to hear. I knew my subconscious was hearing what I needed to hear.

"As he told me later, while I was open Martin poured Love into me and told my higher mind to pour Love in, until I was totally filled with Love. By then we were both crying. When he saw from my physiology that I was completely filled with Love, he reduced the energy to let the reimprint set.

"We grinned happily at each other, and relaxed. When my strength returned, I stood and reaffirmed my two oaths, as Bard and Priest, and closed the circle to end the rite. From the time the energy first rose it had been just 2-¼ hours!

"About a half hour later, energy began running through me again. I felt my crown chakra open, gently as a flower. This energy gradually increased all afternoon; by evening I began to vibrate inside, and became concerned. As Martin and Dara felt my energy, my legs lit up as though I stepped in a live socket. Martin and Dara began running the energy up my legs, slowly and then faster. They ran the energy higher with their hands each time, spreading it from my legs to my hips, then my belly, then my chest, then all the way up my head. I started shaking more rapidly, and the energy began coming up my spine. I recognized that this was probably Kundalini, which I had been trying to activate for years. It arrived as soon as I had become clean and clear.

"Martin reminded me I could use body locks; as I did, the energy became so intense that it shook me from head to foot. When he asked if I was all right, since I was shaking anyway I shook my head yes, so he and Dara would continue distributing the energy throughout my body. After a minute or so that seemed like an hour to me, something opened and the energy went all the way up my spine through my crown. It was like a lightening bolt from earth to sky. Then I stopped shaking, and felt the power was almost under my control again. Emotionally this was one of the most incredible rushes I'd ever had. I hadn't had any idea of what it could be like. Then for a few minutes I had to just sit still and let things stabilize. When I stood up, Martin suggested we dance it in. As we did, I felt more and more comfortable with the energy.

"Then Martin said, 'Let's look at what's happening now.' I stood up behind him, and both physically and psychically I saw energy flowing up his spine as a golden line, a straight line with a red filament through the middle of it. The red filament wasn't real clear but I could see it. He could feel my energy making his more intense as we stood together. Then he stood behind me, we turned back to back, and I started shaking again from our combined energy. In a moment the shaking stopped and I had control of the flow again. I could feel energy flow up from the base of my spine, and I pushed it on up.

"I stayed with Phoenix for four more days, integrating this experience. Each day I got more insights, cried, ran energy, and played my music. Whenever I spoke in the third person, Martin pointed my avoidance out to me. That and my music helped me release more and more emotion. That caused changes deep within my body, and deeper with my Being than I can describe. These kept reopening my energy, until finally it stayed open almost continually.

"When I called my lover, Andrea, she did not recognize my voice. She thought someone was jiving her. Then as she realized my voice had changed so, she was so stunned you could hear her take in her breath in a rush.

"My biochemistry, smell and taste had become more balanced, too. But when I fell back into fear, they changed back instantly. My Phoenix friends picked up that change and taught me to notice it and toggle myself back to balance. They also mirrored my energy shifts in their bodies, and told me where energy was opening and closing in my body, especially whenever my crown chakra blew open again. Thus I learned how to stay aware of my energy changes, and notice how my reality and my energy changed together.

"All in all, it was quite a week."

Conclusion

When Mike returned home, he was able to resume his spiritual growth, and to help others heal through his touch and even activate their subtle energy. Nine months later he wrote: "I also did far more [touch-] healing and had folks asking for my help and advice this year." And "some things that were important no longer seem so... I feel more centered... [W]hen I get down or disgusted with things the spiral is not constantly down into depression, but rather, if I can recognize it... [I can] not only break the cycle, but reverse it. I can get heart space open again, and for the first time in many years I'm at Peace with myself. I WANT more, but I do realize that this is not an overnight process and there is still much work to do and I no longer feel so intimidated by it, and I'm always grateful for those gifts since I did not believe that this much was possible to begin with." Mike and Andrea soon met possible partners for their intentional family; opening the heart attracts others. Mike's Kundalini became intense every few weeks, as he continued to transform. When Mike visited us a third time a year later, he was far clearer, and could go even further—but that's another story.

Suggestions For Further Reading

The following suggestions are for further reading relevant to the innate abilities we all have to mediate causal healing for ourselves and others through transpersonal states of consciousness. For many people the first question is whether such levels of mind and reality exist and, if so, how psychedelics reveal these levels and how they relate to traditional religious and spiritual practices and maps. The work and writing of psychedelic pioneer Stanislav Grof, M.D., squarely addresses these questions. His earlier books such as *LSD Psychotherapy* (Hunter House 1980) and his more recent books such as *Beyond the Brain* (State University of New York Press 1985) all reflect his proposed transpersonal map. The earlier ones emphasize psychedelic therapy and the more recent ones reflect his development of "holotropic therapy" which uses intensified breathing and music. *Spiritual Emergency* (Jeremy P. Tarcher, 1989), which Dr. Grof and his wife Christina edited, and Christina Grof's book *The Stormy Search for Self* (Jeremy P. Tarcher, 1990), focus on intense spontaneous transpersonal experiences and their interpretation as crises or positive psychospiritual transitions. Numerous magazine articles also describe their work.

The Varieties of Psychedelic Experience, by R.E.L. Masters and Jean Houston (Dell 1966), and C.G. Jung's thought and writings, are earlier landmarks from which to gain a perspective on Grof's map.

Another way to compare traditional psychological maps to transpersonal maps is to read Charles Hampden-Turner's *Maps of the Mind* (Collier Books / MacMillan 1981). He offers

60 maps; to us these are largely one-dimensional and sadly limited views of psychology and human potential. Another approach is to read any writings on the twentieth century progression from Freud to Jung to humanistic psychology (especially Maslow) and to transpersonal psychology. Post-Freudian views still have only limited acceptance. This is ironic; the transpersonal maps now struggling for Western acceptance evolved in Eastern thought two to four thousand years ago.

The readings mentioned so far help place "Mike's Story" in the larger context of the transpersonal; the next readings look in the opposite direction of more specifically exploring the dynamics and energies of transpersonal healing.

In *Healers on Healing*, Richard Carlson and Benjamin Shield editors (Jeremy P. Tarcher 1989), 37 leading practitioners of alternative healing address the question "What is the actual cause of healing?" As a physician exploring the power of mind, emotion, love and grace, Bernie S. Siegel, M.D. has written two very popular books, called *Love, Medicine and Miracles* and his sequel *Peace, Love and Healing* (Harper and Row 1989). M. Scott Peck, M.D.'s *The Road Less Travelled* (Touchstone/ Simon and Schuster 1978) discusses the roles of discipline, love, growth and religion, and grace, and has sold three million copies.

Physicians who have turned from conventional medicine to energy-based transpersonal approaches include W. Brugh Joy, M.D., who tells his story in *Joy's Way* (Jeremy P. Tarcher 1979), and Richard Moss, M.D., who has written three books, of which we especially recommend *The Black Butterfly* (Celestial Arts, 1986), in which we find additional richness as our own understanding matures.

There are also many books by non-physicians about learning to detect and mediate subtle energy fields for healing. Of these, Barbara Ann Brennan's *Hands of Light* (Bantam

Books 1987) is unusually thorough in its illustrations and exercises. However, finding a suitable book for developing such skills is a very individualized matter; large bookstores such as the Bodhi Tree in Los Angeles or Yes! Bookstore in Washington, D.C. are invaluable sources and can be consulted by phone.

Three fundamental models to be compared are (1) the "patient / healer" model; (2) the "shamanic" model; and, we add, (3) the "co-equal participant" model.

In the conventional Western "healer/ patient" model the healer does not accompany the patient into altered consciousness. Also, Western psychology does not countenance any psychologist accompanying any patient into altered consciousness, especially through psychedelics. Also, causal healing is given labels such as spontaneous remission which obscure the inner ability to remit disease and to develop wellness and vitality at many levels. The study of vastly broader health paradigms could thus complement and radically advance healing sciences, technologies and arts.

In shamanic traditions the shaman usually took a psychedelic whether or not the patient did, and always had special abilities in altered consciousness. It is an ancient view, thought radical in our society, that the shaman (doctor / priest / guide / visionary) can take the medicine and the patient can heal. Books we recommend regarding shamanism include the now-classic *Hallucinogens and Shumanism,* Michael J. Harner editor (Oxford University Press 1973) and Roger Walsh's new book *The Spirit of Shamanism* (Jeremy P. Tarcher, 1990)

"Mike's Story" reports two examples of the third model, in which two or more people have a series of progressive transpersonal experiences together for progressive healing, growth and transformation guided by subtle energy and its phenomena such as archetypes rather than by Western or shamanic diagnosis, treatment and belief systems. The energy

itself is the physician / psychologist / shaman, is the diagnos-
tician and the treatment, and is a teacher and evolutionary
force. This attributes causal healing and for that matter life
and evolution to what may be called a subtle energy, or love,
or consciousness itself. We experience it as energy, archetypes, dynamics and processes which have its or their own
innate intelligence and which heal and transform those who
seek it, according to their individual needs. In this model
healing, growth and transformation are fundamentally similar
(like progressive inches on a yardstick), and operate by many
of the same dynamics. Any individual can explore this through
meditation, yoga, psychedelics or other means, but groups of
two or more people can also explore it by inducting each
other to shared transpersonal states of consciousness and by
mediating processes beyond the present limits of medicine
and psychology. Induction is known in electromagnetism,
and is thus to be expected as an aspect of subtle energy
fields. (An analogy in mechanics is the tendency of pendu-
lum clocks to synchronize their periods; a Jungian analogy is
the concept of synchrony.)

There is a dearth of literature and research on these facets
of human potential. Issue 3 of *Psychedelic Monographs and
Essays* (1988), which members of Phoenix Research Foundation guest edited, was a theme issue on psychedelics and
spirituality (and psychedelic research) and included several
articles of relevance. In *ReVision* 10(4) (Spring 1988), a
theme issue called "Psychedelics Revisited," the article "From
Mysteries to Paradigms: Humanity's Journey From Sacred
Plants to Psychedelic Drugs" by Richard Yensen is an excellent summary of past and prospective models of psychedelics
and healing. *Psychedelic Monographs and Essays,* "Mike's
Story" and the ongoing work of Phoenix Research Foundation all address altered consciousness and what it offers

to enrich life and hopefully to contribute to the global future.

Many people will find that by reading a book or article which describes any type of transpersonal experience, such as those cited above or leading books on Zen, and then asking their mind to generate such an experience, they can have such an experience. This amounts to conditioning their personal expectation, or "set," which helps determine perceptions and experiences.

AMAZONIAN SHAMANISM: THE AYAHUASCA EXPERIENCE

By Dr. Thomas Pinkson

I am a psychologist in private practice, a business consultant to executive and management groups on high performance, and I am also a clinical consultant with a Center working since 1976 with children and families facing life threatening illness. Another involvement since 1972 has been taking people up into the mountains on vision quest retreats. These usually last six days, including a 2 to 4 day period of solitude and fasting, seeking deeper vision. I've been going to the same spot for 20 years now. It takes two days backpacking in, including a demanding climb over an 11,000 foot mountain, but once there it is worth the effort. It's off the beaten track and there is usually nobody else there but a beautiful lake, thick woods and surrounding peaks of granite jutting sharply up into the sky. Yet as beautiful as it is, I found myself wondering if it was time to go to a different site for a change. But then last year's quest was so powerful, including two double rainbows right as we were doing ceremony on our final two nights in the mountains, that I got the message: *Keep coming back here for the rest of your life. If you live long enough, and really open up while here, then perhaps you'll learn just a little of what is available to you in this special place of power.*

I went back again just a few weeks ago with another group for six days and I am continually amazed by the deepening richness available by returning to the same sacred place. An increasing wealth of information comes through with direct relevance to whatever it is we are seeking when we go out on a quest in a good way.

Part of this has to do with the phenomenon of bioentrainment. The primary energy coming into us during the quest is directly from nature. Gradually we become attuned to the rhythms of nature and begin to function as natural beings in a natural world. One of the ways that is noticeable is when we hike back out of the mountains a week later. As we get closer to civilization we start running into rhythms and patterns that are not in harmony and balance, more people, garbage, noise and pollution. We start to get irritable, as if we're going through a withdrawal of some kind and in fact we are. The whole notion of bioentrainment is fundamental to understanding shamanism. For the shaman knows how to willfully change channels of awareness and entrain themselves into state specific knowledge available therein. Our culture teaches us but a few of these changes. The shaman knows many.

One of the experiences on this last retreat was looking back on how many of my blood relatives had died recently. I missed them. Yet on a quest I noticed how the rocks, the trees, the mountains, the lake, and the same circle I sit in seeking that deeper vision over all these years were all becoming increasingly familiar to me. This time they spoke: *We are your aunts and uncles, your relatives, your family. We are your true Elders, the old ones. We have much to teach you when you take the time to really listen.* I have been listening and in this article I want to share my "conversation" with one particular family of Elders—power plants. In the traditional cultures I've spent time with, including the Huicholes of Mexico since 1981, and more recently in the Amazon jungle, and the Andes mountains with indigenous shaman there, the use of power plants as Elders is integral to their shamanic ways. The plants are considered gifts from Mother Earth's body that have specific purpose. If you come into the right relationship with them, with respect, they can take you through the "nierika," the doorway, into mystical states of transpersonal knowledge and power.

Yesterday, I was reading an interview with a mathematician who was talking about the notion of different dimensions in space called "worm holes." The article discussed the theoretical possibility of entering those "worm holes" to travel from one dimension to another. The Huicholes and Amazon shaman have been doing this experientially for thousands of years. Through right relationships with power plants in sacred ceremony they move through the doorway into the Great Mystery to gain guidance and power. In the shamanic tradition, it is important to emphasize that the work with psychoactive plants is not for the purpose of escapism, denial or irresponsible acting out behavior. Rather it is for the purpose of getting hold of something to bring back to the people, not just for yourself. You bring something back for your people. This was for the purpose of your journey, to get something useful and practical that can make a difference in your life and the betterment of the lives of your people and all your relationships. Todos unidos! All united, the Huicholes say over and over again.

The plant people are respected Elders revered much as devotees feel toward their guru. My experience with the Huicholes and some of the people in the Amazon is that they have the same kind of love and awe for their plant elders, their medicine teachers and guides, as followers of Christ or Buddha have for theirs!

So I want to say a few words about one of these Elders, yagé or ayahuasca, which is used in many parts of the Amazon. It is actually a drink, a mixture of several different plants. The pharmacological sophistication of the shamans of the Amazon is incredible. They are living in this richest area of psychoactive plants in the world. Until the last 100 years they were pretty much left alone. So we're talking about an unbroken tradition, handed down from generation to generation going back ten, fifteen, twenty thousand years or more of research and development, where the gains that are achieved by one generation are passed on to the next and then built on. Depending on what the shaman wants to facilitate in terms of the experience, he takes a bit of this leaf; with another experience he takes a little bit of a different leaf or flower. They have a highly developed understanding of the synergy of these plants that in various combinations can facilitate the kind of healing experience they want to produce for an individual.

The vine ingredient of the ayahuasca brew, Banistereopsis caapi, is considered to be the masculine energy and the Chakruna leaves bring the feminine. The shaman fine tunes the mixture with varying quantities and add-mixtures depending on their goal. Ayahuasca is not an easy experience. It has a strong purgative effect so that you can be cleaned out on both ends. It is not mild or gentle. It can be projectile vomiting. It can be tough. The native people welcome the cleansing. With all the intestinal worms in the Amazon, it cleans you out that way. They also feel it produces emotional, psychic and spiritual cleansing as well. Children take it too. At one particular session, there were three Indian children with us who had not had an ayahuasca experience. They had their first experience standing there with family and the rest of us, vomiting. The Indians believe the purging opens the doorway to visions, so they welcome it. It is fascinating that the shamans say one of the ways they learn about new plants is through the guidance from ayahuasca.

In my first experience with ayahuasca, plants of the jungle did appear before me and speak, just as the shamans report happens with them. The problem was that I did not understand their language! I knew they were giving me information but I wasn't conversant in their language and so didn't get it. It takes a period of time to learn the language of the plants. Most shamans were introduced to the plants through their own illness or wounding. They were ill or injured in some way when they were young and were introduced to ayahuasca through a healing ceremony. It was not a teacher for them until a number of sessions took place over time. Then the spirit of the plant opened up to them and began to relate to them as a teacher. Part of this process was learning the language. Another part is enduring the repeated purges. It is not easy.

A Brazilian ayahuasca group I've worked with says that you cannot have light without the shadow. It is a full circle. If you step into these ways, you have to pay some dues. You cannot take without giving. This has a grounding effect.

I am especially interested in the "intelligence" of the power plants like ayahuasca. It is prelinguistic intelligence connected with transcendent realms of knowing that do not fit easily into western thought categories.

One ayahuasca vision showed me how every level of existence, including material and non-material levels as thoughts or feelings, have vibration, or sound underneath their surface manifestation. If one can reproduce the sound, vibration, or "song" of that which you are working with, you can enter into it and change it around! The shaman does just this using themselves as an instrument to effect the joining.

This information came in handy in a recent experience working with life threatening illness. Through this work I see that real healing always takes place through joining. When we are able to dissolve separation to experience our one-ness, healing is the result. My ayahuasca experience showed me one away, a most ancient way to gain entry and create joining. Once you are "in," the question becomes what do you want to do; what is your intentionality, your purpose in being there to begin with. I have explored this experience of joining through chanting, drumming, prayer, ceremony, med-itation, and most recently through song. I want to share one of my recent explorations on this realm with an AIDS patient. He was a 40-year-old artist, very bright and animated. When I first met him, he was terribly frightened of being alone, of death and that he was going to be put in a black box forever. He was paralyzed by his fear and in tremendous pain, taking enough morphine to kill three or four people but still not working for him. He was full of anger and felt abandoned by friends and family. He'd also alienated the medical staff in one hospital to where they would not let him in without a guard for the nurses. Underneath this all he was a wonderfully sensitive person with deep integrity who wanted to find inner peace so he could die with dignity and without fear. I worked with him for six months, visiting him at home or in the hospital up until the day before his death.

On what was to be our last visit I watched him laboring to breathe with an oxygen mask on his face, exhausted from the ravages of disease and disoriented by pain medication and sedation. I focused all my attention on opening my heart and extending love. I visualized myself as a section of pipe hooked up to the "Great Generator," just playing my part in the linkup process. The pipe gets blocked when we think we are doing it all. But when we get ego mind out of the way we really can be a channel for a healing love force.

While silently holding his hand and sending him love, I began to enter a trance state. Up from the depths of my mind came the words of a song that I'd learned in Mexico years before while on a pilgrimage with the Huichole Indians. I adopted it as my "death song" and had used it once before as a dear friend was dying. Now it felt like the song wanted to be sung again. My first response was not to do it. "How will he receive it?" I worried. Then I remembered the ayahuasca teaching from the Amazon about joining through sound. The guidance grew stronger. "Just sing it, just share the song," it said. "Just send it to him, without any pressure or attachment. Sing it to him with love and let it go," said the inner instructions. So softly I began to hum. Slowly the humming shifted into singing, soft at first, then louder, As I sang louder, I could hear him trying to hum along. Then to my total surprise, he took off his oxygen mask and began to sing along with me. He had barely enough strength to breathe, but somehow found strength to join me in singing. Singing together our voices became one as we both sang louder. Then a phase shift occurred and there was no separation between us; we were one! His eyes came to life, his face now radiant. For the first time since I knew him he was joyful. He was experiencing what he had been so desperately seeking so that he could die in peace—release from fear and union with spirit. It was a transcendent experience for us both. Our hearts and souls joined together in a timeless moment of absolute bliss. This was the culmination of our work together. We stayed in silence for several minutes enjoying the awe of what had just touched us both so powerfully.

Shortly thereafter, it was time for me to leave. Previously he would become very anxious whenever I would leave after one of our sessions. "Make sure you come back. You are coming back, aren't you?" he'd ask worriedly. This time he released effortlessly. We gave each other a long hug and said goodbye. He smiled as I left the room and died the next day. The teachings from the "Elders" had served us well.

WALTER BENJAMIN
AND THE
DRUG VISION

by Kenda Willey

The claim that natural highs are preferable to drug-induced ones can be argued against by the fact that natural highs are usually induced by specifically directed energy output, instead of fanning out to include the spectrum of factors that might demand and receive attention by a person on a drug trip. The relaxing or performance-heightening qualities of hallucinogens are, indeed, slight or even negative, but no non-religious ecstasy can surpass the consciousness- and knowledge-raising potential of hallucinogens.

A natural high is more the product of the ego than is a chemically produced one. No hallucinogen-experienced person will claim to have mastered the drug during the experience, rather their achievement will be to have "gone with it." Visions are never produced by conscious will: this is meant in the sense that while taking drugs, fasting or meditating are certainly conscious efforts that make for visions, it is the visions that "come over one."

I would like to weaken the apparent contradiction between this sentence and the above-mentioned "specifically directed energy output" involved in natural highs: highs are heightened consciousness, visions are...well, visions are what can happen in the state of heightened consciousness. Wherever there is stoned vision, there is heightened meeting up with self-expressing things, but the less concentration involved in bringing the high about, the greater the possible diffusion of vision. Visions' form and content are not produced at will, but can be described as the result of altered access to outside influences, whereby the role of the outside influences should not be underestimated—they are, after all, "active" in taking advantage of the alteration. This psychologized concept of vision is one of the main thematics of Benjamin's writings on drug experience.

> "Whereas in our normal condition, the pictures we ignore completely will remain subconscious, with hashish, pictures do not seem to require our attention whatsoever in order to present themselves to us."
>
> (Walter Benjamin, GS VI, p. 589)
> (citation translated by the authoress)

A drug experience may make the person "tender to things." Lack of ambition is conducive to a successful drug experience, causing the ego to recede from the foreground, making room for a flood of the linguistic entities we call things of nature.

Another kind of knowledge

The de-psychologized version of perception which distinguishes Benjamin's philosophy of language takes on even stronger features when it comes to drug experience: instead of emphasizing the role of social determinants or mentality in the drug trip, his main objects of interest were the role of the things perceived, our insight into their self-expression, and our limited possibilities of speaking of them.

Walter Benjamin...

The German Jewish philosopher Walter Benjamin (1892–1940) took part in several drug experiments under controlled circumstances. Though extensive drug experience has been rumored, it is beside the point here. The fact that he did take part in hashish and mescaline experiments and wrote about it, the fact that some of his essays—that on French Surrealism, for example—are laced with references to drug experience, and the fact that he committed suicide by a probable morphine overdose suffice as basis for rumours of addiction, irregardless of the frequency with which the man actually indulged.

The recorded drug experiments in which Benjamin took part (other participants were Fritz Fraenkel and Ernst Joel as supervising doctors, Gert and Egon Wissing, and Ernst Bloch and Benjamin as experimental subjects) are not only handed down to us as protocols, but also in the form of written recapitulations by the experimental subjects. Not only Benjamin's method of working, but his extensive travels and also the fugitive life he led in the last few years of his life left behind a mass of fragments and incomplete writings. His method of working involved the near-endless gathering of quotes, notes, allegories and cross-references on little cards and pieces of paper; starting off on projects which were eventually laid aside, to be resumed months or years later, then rewritten due to the influence exerted by friends or new theories upon him—Benjamin was very susceptible to criticism, and constructive suggestions by friends were taken very much to heart, sometimes to the extent of delaying completion of a project, and, in the case of his legendary Arcades Project, he switched from a very literary style in the first draft to one more heavily influenced by historical materialism in the second. Benjamin's torment by self-doubt was complemented by financial and professional insecurity throughout his career; he never obtained the cherished academic position that would have granted him the financial cushion necessary for continuity in his work.

Perhaps the great variety of the fields he wrote about was partly responsible for the incompleteness and openendedness of his *oeuvre*. What was definitely also responsible for the fragmentary character of what we know of Benjamin's writings is his persecution by and flight from the Nazis: during his exile in Paris in the 1930's, much of what he produced ended up somewhere or other—in Paris, Moscow, Palestine, often with friends—some of it never turning up again. His Arcades Project, the masterpiece that would hopefully have assured his reputation, either remained unfinished or disappeared in the confusion of flight and hiding in Nazi-occupied France. Benjamin himself died in the confusion: having crossed the border into Spain, he was arrested in the north Spanish harbour town of Port Bou and prevented by the Spanish authorities from boarding a ship leaving Europe. Informed that his flight from France had been illegal and that he would be extradited back to France, Benjamin committed suicide. What has been published of the Arcades Project are his notes and drafts, not the final version.

Altogether, it becomes obvious that Benjamin was not the only one at fault for the disappearance of his work. But the fact remains that Benjamin often worked against himself, that his lack of success was a result not only of his nonconformity, but his neuroses.

...and his drug experience

Benjamin saw in the drug experience the location where things of nature, otherwise mournful in their speechlessness, turned almost petulant in their insistence to be heard. He did not, however, postulate a human ability to actually hear these things' language in full, but rather a Baudelairian murmuring, and he expressly denied the lingual capability of "translating" whatever murmurs can be heard, of passing them on. They will, according to Benjamin, never be understood though they may be heard, somehow...and how they are heard must be both intuitive and based on long-forgotten knowledge. To call any kind of knowledge "intuitive" is a departure from Benjamin; he never even hinted at recognition of things being anything but the result of knowledge implanted long ago.

His argumentation on this point is heavily theological, even exegetic. Still, he was not just speaking allegorically: for him, the language of things is without question something that humankind has known, because humankind once partook of divine language (divine being definable as beyond the human language and therefore foreign to experience, or—taking Benjamin literally—divine because Godly).

His drug-related writings do not go into this in any detail; a full explanation is contained in his early philosophy of language. It involves the self-reflecting word in divine language and the birth of the human language. Benjamin's early philosophy of language has the language of every thing except Adam and Eve consisting solely in its name. Though mute, i.e. not gifted with own language, things were gifted with a self-reflexive name, thus eliminating necessity of (verbal) language. Humankind did not receive its name from God, but rather received the power of original or divine language, and then named itself and all other things for—in the name of—God. The joy of creatures upon receiving names that were *le mot juste* is contrasted with the deep sorrow of nature about its muteness under the yoke of human language.

The tree of knowledge, insidiously placed inside the garden of Eden all the time, smuggled the devastating word of judgement into paradise, dividing between good and evil, getting Adam and Eve thrown out of the garden, necessitating labor and subjugation of nature and eventually separating everything from its name. In other words, human language is arbitrary and guided by interests, i.e. the fragmentation of the world, while divine language is not. It is not only a matter of new words, but it involves two very different organizations of thought, and they cannot be brought together.

Perception of things of nature remains and will remain unclear, communication about them roundabout or nonverbal, and, most important, never successful, never doing them justice. Benjamin was anything but reactionary, though, and he did not propose a return to origins. His messianic marxism tended to be hurtling, far removed from step-by-step dialectics, but rather full of surprises, such as the still-stand as revolutionary, jumping off the rails of history. His hypothesized dichotomy between the two languages is depressingly unmendable, with the only hope lying in experimental approaches towards "translating"—drugs being one of these approaches.

In illustrating his view of the barriers to perception, at the same time Benjamin the phenomonologist illustrates that the richest expressivity lies within the barriers themselves: he compares it with the layers of an onion, where the outer parts hide the core and at the same time express so much of it. It is the layers of the onion, not its heart (which is humanly inaccessible) that gives us an understanding of the onion; it is the ornamentation, the frills that express the spirit of the thing, and not the other way around. Our vision or understanding of a thing is our perception of what appears to us. And what appears to us is the expression, or self-expression of us, not of what we describe; our means of approaching the self-expression of things is also the source of the fundamental injustice done when speaking of them.

This fits in with the definition of mysticism that describes it as a search for supernal truth, inachievable because of the infinite number of truths still standing between the searcher and divine truth. Benjamin's friend, the Kabbala scholar Gersholm Scholem, called Jewish messianism a catastrophe theory, a striving towards a fulfillment that appears unlikely to happen. This serves as an excellent nutshell description of Benjamin's messianic philosophy.

Be it early or late in Benjamin's life, his theories were vested with, indeed they *suffered* from, a strong sense of elusiveness of goals. For example, his interpretation of the origin of language in the garden of Eden has God planting the very tree that gets Adam and Eve thrown out of paradise. In other words, they could have never stayed innocent, and there is no way back.

Divine and Human Language

Human language is the means of differentiating between important and less important, and is in this sense instrumental in constructing a hierarchy; this is not true of the supposed divine language in which equality reigns instead of judgement, and everything can exist and be respected in its own right (its own name).

"...things are, as we all know, technicalized, rationalized, and...specialness nowadays can only be found in nuances,

(but) yesterday's insight was quite the contrary: I saw only
nuances, and they were all the same."

(GS VI, p. 585)
(citation translated by the authoress)

Here, in human language, is where identity is split into
non-identity, where being ceases to be identical with idea.
Things are reduced to an incidental product of thought, in
contrast to the self-reflexive (fully self-describing) name in
which the idea is commensurate with its being.

According to Benjamin, many paths connect the instrumen-
talization of nature with the arbitrariness of human language:
the loss of self-reflexiveness of language, separation of subject from object and therefore of the speaker and his object,
even the speaker from his speech, the word from meaning
and meaning from what's meant. Robbed of the proper
name, nature has no tongue to express herself (and, to quote
Irving Wohlfarth in his excellent article on Benjamin, nature
as conceived by Benjamin is "too Jewish" not to strive towards language).

Language becomes a speaking about things according to
how interesting they are, a narrowing of horizons takes
place, a concentration on the relevant, the pertinent. Things
are judged by fashionableness, utility and desirability. Awareness
of the world of contingencies is one thing, actually doing
them justice and living with them means indiscriminate
acceptance of their total equality, making no choices between
them, floating in the world of contingencies. An admirable
solidarity with things, but hardly practicable in everyday life.
Consciousness of contingencies demands a compromise. Stoned
consciousness is impractible in ongoing life about to the
same degree that the banishment of drug visions to the
nether world is disrespectful. A compromise must provide a

way that their shadow can fall upon our sober, everyday lives. And a way must be found to put them into words.

The "pathos of nearness" expounded in another context by Benjamin is applicable here: instead of empathy with things, which is an out-going, downward-looking sympathy, the pathos of nearness comprises allowing things to enter into one's life. In other words to best put them into words, they must first be allowed to speak. This is where Benjamin saw the sense of drug experience: he praised it as a "propedeutic" (preparatory) to consciousness-raising.

Speaking of drug experience

Knowledge of things passes through the stage of metaphor very early in the process of recognition: obtaining knowledge of things this way is part of our organization of knowledge. With increasing familiarity with the idea of the thing, the metaphoric description loses importance, serving as secondary (instead of primary) sign. We nevertheless retain metaphors not only in our spoken language, but also in our perception of things. This is particularly the case when materialistic language meets up with intangibles, or with ideas uncommon to everyday experience, and therefore unfamiliar to common language. Whereas Benjamin did not consider the human-language words for things to be entirely coincidental, this did not prevent him from sometimes saying just the opposite, and eventually meeting himself in the middle.

The difficulty of explaining drug experience is exemplary for the unwinnable struggle to hook common language up with uncommon experience and is at the same time, a good place to start: Benjamin does not resign to this quandary, but rather recommends expressing them by speaking in *Abbruch* ("broken-off", meaning incongruous or indirect reference to the subject at hand) when confronted with the task of describing visions.

> "It is a common characteristic of hashish highs that speaking is accompanied by a kind of resignation, that the stoned person has already foregone speaking of what really moves him, and that he tries instead to put something incidental and unserious in the place of the unnameable essential, that is far from seldom that he feels guilty of injustice in speaking, and that—and this is what's curious and demands explanation—the thus interrupted expression may be much stranger and profounder than what would actually correspond to "what was meant."
>
> (Joel or Fraenkel, GS VI, p. 601)
> (citation translated by the authoress)

Abbruch includes synesthesia (the juxtaposition of sensual experience, such as hearing a color), autotelic statement ("focussing on the way it is expressed," to quote Roman Jakobson), incomplete sentences, paradoxes and metaphoric or esoteric references to experiences foreign to the vision as the only ways of getting around the impossibility of linking our language with visionary language—which is, in the end, the language of things. And so we have the impossibility of translating drug visions into language, and at the same time the desire to do so. Or even the duty to do so—here, Benjamin mixes the love that drug visions can inspire together with the solidarity *demanded* by the disenfranchised.

The Material Community Speaks

"It is as if words were being fed into one phonetically. This is spontaneous (automatic) connection. Things speak up without even asking permission. It continues on up into the highest spheres. There's a silent password that lets certain things enter the gate."

(Ernst Bloch, in: GS VI, p. 566)
(citation translated by the authoress)

In addition to what drugs tells us about ourselves, there is a whole material community of things clamoring for attention during drug experience. Benjamin has them flouncing about, flirting and thumping one about the shoulders in best anthropomorphic manner. The key word here is "material": this is the point where stoned and sober states can become mutual, if not interchangeable. Hallucinogenic insight does not have to be abandoned when the vision is over: be it truth or illusion (nature is capable of playing tricks), examination of such insight for applicability in ongoing life is responsible use of drugs. Responsible not only towards oneself as a social being, but also toward the drug. Deification of drugs is too esoteric to do them justice; drugs are no longer what they were in the days of their religious use. To vest nature with unchanging character would be to misjudge her: she is as much subject to (sub*jected* to) her history as is anything else. In other words, she is no longer divine nature, she is transformed by use and abuse.

"...icon for the faithful, a windfall for the glib, a bonus for under-employed experts, a thrill for the naive, a whipping-boy for the ambitious, a tool for mystic explorers, a tantalizing mystery for scientists, a cash crop for peasants; hassles, joy, shouting, tranquility, apoplexy, fear, rebellion all wash over Western man in the presence of the little green weed..."

(Wm. Daniel Drake, Jr., cited from Psychedelics Encyclopedia by Peter Stafford, S. 85)

Drugs are among the most badly abused things nature has to offer. With nature's subjugation through humankind, her simple self-reflexivity has ceased to dominate the picture, her functions have been multiplied and transformed. Drugs have taken the same path: no longer the fetish, charm or medicine of the past, drugs have gone through so much that they can more easily be associated with oppression, anaesthetization, suicide and death. Drugs are among the most badly warped things nature has to offer.

Their functions are manifold: not only are they part of nature, but they are goods on the market. The fact that drugs can tyrannize, that our very humanity can be pummeled and perverted in the grip of chemical substances (or in the grip of the fear that they inspire, as in anti-drug politics), suffice to qualify drugs as nature's revenge upon humankind. Indeed, over the past few hundred years drugs have always been punishing someone somewhere: both opium and cocoa have been used to brutalize and colonize countries, and both opium and cocaine have flowed from these countries into the occident to strike fear into the hearts of the exploiters.

Remembrance of the "other drugs" of the past recalls to mind what drugs were and can (also) be, but can never cancel what they now are—no revision of drug history. It seems strange that things that were once no danger are now a danger, and that, meanwhile, mastery over drugs can only be obtained by eradication of drugs. The conflict is how much resistance against nature may be necessary to offset her violence against humankind. Absolute love of all natural phenomena is nothing but the opposite pole to the concept of nature as a system consisting of functions obviously useful for us.

Adoration of nature without self-assertion seems as much a misunderstanding as does enjoyment of nature without respect for her. The same applies for drugs. Drug use without consequences is a banalization of drugs—something of the disenfranchised should rub off by association, sympathy and solidarity is the suitable reaction—Benjamin goes as far as to claim that their very deprivation rubs off on one.

Nature: Utopias or essential suffering?

"Is it, then, sheer utopianism—to claim to take 'the side of things' (...)? Is the 'complaint' of a personified nature anything more than a case of projection motivated by pity and guilt?")

(Irving Wohlfarth, p. 200)

Mankind, however tender and attentive, will never do nature justice: he (as opposed to the she of nature) cannot. However he attempts to speak for nature, he misses her by a long shot. It is one thing to acknowledge the meaning of nature for oneself, and another to solidarize with her. The loss of an aesthetic surrounding, the increase in allergies, the skin cancer and melting icebergs caused by a hole in the ozone is something different than the torment of nature herself. It is possible that a nature gifted with language would not raise the same accusations as humankind does. After all, it is generally accepted as true that nature does not suffer starting with the death of trees or the extinction of a species, but rather that her suffering starts much earlier on. As Benjamin would have it, nature started suffering right away: she did not suffer until after Adam and Eve's expulsion from paradise, but she was doomed to suffer the moment the tree of knowledge was planted in the garden, and her without a means to protect herself. According to Benjamin, it is her muteness and lack of rights under human language that she mourns, and this far predates industrial waste.

This muteness is the essential difference between humankind and nature. Humankind is not only part of nature, he is her opponent. According to Benjamin, humankind had from the very beginning ascendancy over the rest of nature. The ascendancy is meanwhile corrupt, humankind has separated himself from nature. But unconditional solidarity with a being driven to desperation can be risky: nature and drugs have not remained unchanged by the treatment they have suffered. Benjamin's definition of the muteness and mourning of nature includes the hint that, if nature did have a language, she would not be upright and sovereign, but would wail and keen in a way suiting a low level of consciousness. Viewing nature as a conscious being is the middle-of-the-road between suspicion and surrender to nature.

Looking around for comparisons among current attitudes toward nature, this fits in best with the "ecologist" movement: The environmentalist view of nature involves conservation of the functions of nature necessary for human production and reproduction, not only such natural resources as go into industry, but also the functions conducive to human comfort, aesthetic enjoyment and the upholding of traditions.

This stands in sharp contrast to reverence of nature inherent to the ecologist view: the anthropomorphic investment with essential being, even a cohesive personality—this in opposition to the view of nature as a collection of various flora and fauna adapted to surroundings and therefore balanced-out—and the sense of duty and solidarity with nature as with other oppressed creatures, are the common ground of ecologism and Benjamin's mystical philosophy of language.

It is my opinion that Benjamin meant with "pathos of nearness" not only lingual phenomena, but that he was also implying consequences: that the language of things would, by flowing into one's own language—in other words, by translation of visions into one's own language—change the relationship to one's environment; that Benjamin was also talking about affinity with, and affection and care of material things (and here he meant not only nature—he expressly included goods). Here is where an "environmentalist" view of nature as the sum of her functions ceases to be applicable and the "ecologist" view of nature as conscious presents itself as the only alternative.

All reports of psychedelic experiences are filled with impressions of nature pressing in upon the person stoned enough to listen to her in tender silence. Drugs are a medium between nature and humankind: they are things of nature speaking to us in their own right, and have an unusual power to jumble our mentality. If it can be claimed that nature has been subjugated to the point of begging for mercy, then what can be held against any medium that facilitates understanding her? If you believe she speaks, that is. Or is in need of language-gifted defense. If she has a state of being, she is necessarily an object of language—in fact, she's a victim of it.

To defend her for purposes of one's own self-satisfaction, or out of unconditional love, does not do justice—the more we know about systems, the more obvious it is that solidarity without understanding can well finish the job that cruel repression started—what she needs is to be known to us, if it is not possible for her to be equal to us.

Bibliography

Benjamin, Andrew, *"Tradition and Experience: Walter Benjamin's 'On some Motifs in Baudelaire'"*, pp. 122-140 in: Benjamin, Andrew (ed.), *The Problems of Modernity. Adorno and Benjamin*, London and New York 1989.

Benjamin, Walter/Ernst Bloch/Fritz Fraenkel and Ernst Joel (all authors of drug experiment protocols) on pp. 558-618 in: Hermann Schweppenhaeuser and Rolf Tiedemann (eds.),

Walter Benjamin. Gesammelte Schriften VI, Frankfurt am Main 1985.

Menninghaus, Winfried, *Walter Benjamins Theorie der Sprachmagie*, Frankfurt am Main 1980.

Michaux, Henri, *Miserable Miracle,* San Francisco 1963.

Schweppenhaeuser, Hermann, *"Die Vorschule der profanen Erleuchtung,"* (Foreword) pp 7-30 in: Rexroth, Tilmann (ed.), *Walter Benjamin. Ueber Haschisch,* Frankfurt am Main 1972.

Stafford, Peter, *Psychedelics Encyclopedia*, Berkeley/Cal, 1979.

Wohlfarth, Irving, *"On some Jewish Motifs in Benjamin,"* pp. 157-215 in: Benjamin, Andrew (ed.), *The Problems of Modernity. Adorno and Benjamin,* London and New York 1989.

APPARENT COMMUNICATION WITH DISCARNATE ENTITIES INDUCED BY DIMETHYLTRYPTAMINE (DMT)

by Peter Meyer

...and in search for answers people have feared to place themselves on the line and to actually wrestle with life and death out there in those strange, bardo-like dimensions, not realizing that there is no other way to win true knowledge...

—Terence McKenna
Psilocybin and the Sands of Time

1. Tryptamine psychedelics

In this article I wish to draw attention to a strange property of the tryptamine psychedelics, especially N,N-dimethyltryptamine (DMT), which sets them apart from other psychedelics, namely, their ability to place users in touch with a realm that is apparently inhabited by discarnate entities of an intelligent nature. The investigation of such a possibility clearly takes us to (and perhaps beyond) the fringes of what is considered scientifically acceptable. Nevertheless, the phenomenon of apparent alien contact is so impressive to those who have experienced it, and the implications of such contact are so radical, that the evidence deserves serious investigation.

The term "psychedelic" may be understood to denote a class of substances whose primary effect is to alter consciousness in an ego-transcending manner so that the experience of a person whose neurochemistry is altered by such a substance is enhanced and expanded in comparison with ordinary experience. This enhancement and expansion may be emotional, intellectual, intuitive, sensory, spiritual or somatic. The qualification that the experience involve a tendency to ego transcendence is added partly to distinguish substances such as LSD and MDMA from stimulants such as amphetamine and cocaine and partly because it is one of the more remarkable properties of psychedelics that, by their means, we may enter mythological and spiritual dimensions not normally the concern of our everyday selves.

Psychedelics may be classified most easily in two ways: according to their effect on consciousness or according to their chemical structure. The former is difficult to quantify, and the data here tends to be of a literary nature (e.g., Horowitz [56]). Due to the regrettable proscription of the use of psychedelics in many countries, and to the suppression of research in this field, not much has been published during the last 20 years regarding the effects of psychedelics on consciousness. With the increasing recognition in more enlightened societies of the potential value of psychedelics we may hope to see a renewal of publication in this area.

The structural classification lends itself to quantitative scientific investigation. From such work as has been permitted in this field it seems that, for the most part, "hallucinogens are divided into two separate categories. The first... covers the substituted phenylalkylamines, with the prototype for these structures being mescaline. The second category includes indole-based compounds, including various substituted tryptamines, beta-carbolines, and LSD" (Nichols [81], p. 97). Not all psychedelics fall into these two categories. Ketamine is clearly a psychedelic but is structurally unrelated to the phenethylamines or to the tryptamines.

The most well-known psychedelic tryptamines consist of DMT and three variations on it:

5-methoxy-DMT	=	5-MeO-DMT
4-hydroxy-DMT	=	psilocin
4-phosphoryloxy-DMT	=	psilocybin

Psilocybin is converted to psilocin in the body. The corresponding diethyltryptamine analogs are similarly psychoactive (and reportedly longer lasting). Psychoactivity has been reported in alpha-methyltryptamine (Murphree [79]), 4-methoxy-DMT and 5-methoxy-alpha-methyltryptamine (Nichols [81]) and bufotenine, which is 5-hydroxy-DMT (Fabing [23] and Turner [126]). 6-hydroxy-DMT has been reported as one of the excretory metabolites of DMT (Szara [118]). A review of the literature will reveal a considerable number of other tryptamine derivatives which either are known to be or may be psychoactive.

Although LSD is not a tryptamine, its molecular structure includes that of the tryptamine molecule. We cannot thereby simply classify it as a tryptamine psychedelic because its molecular structure also includes that of some psychedelic phenethylamines such as 2,5-dimethoxy-4-methyl-amphetamine (DOM) (Nichols [81], p. 114). Nevertheless, LSD is usually classified with the tryptamine psychedelics and seems more closely related to them because it is more readily displaced from receptor sites by the tryptamines than by the phenethylamines.

DMT has been found to occur naturally in mammalian brains (Barker [4] and Christian [17]. "Indolealkylamines... are the only known hallucinogenic agents whose endogenous occurrence in mammals, including man, has been confirmed" (McKenna [67]). Szara [114] says that it "seems that the whole enzymatic apparatus exists in mammals which can produce tryptamine from tryptophane, DMT from tryptamine and 6-HDMT [the probably hallucinogenic 6-hydroxy-DMT] from DMT."

The question as to what function DMT and related substances have in the mammalian body has not yet received a definite answer. DMT is structurally similar to serotonin (5-hydroxytryptamine) which is well-known as a neurotransmitter in the mammalian brain. It has been suggested that DMT is also a neurotransmitter, but this has not been established. Strassman [110] has presented evidence that psychoactive tryptamines are produced endogenously by the pineal gland and are related to the metabolism of the pineal hormone melatonin. Clearly much research in this area remains to be done.

2. DMT usage

(a) Shamanic usage

The history of human involvement with DMT probably goes back many thousands of years since DMT usage is associated with South American shamanism. Stafford [108] mentions that the "Spanish friar Ramón Paul, who accompanied Columbus on his second voyage to the New World, was the first to record native use of... 'kohhobba' to communicate with the spirit world" (p. 310). A series of distinguished ethnobotanists eventually established that the psychoactive ingredients of these native snuffs (known under various names, including *cohoba, yopo,* and *epaná*) were obtained from plants such as *Anadenanthera macrocarpa*, formerly *peregrina* (Schultes [95] and Harner [48]). Chemists then showed that the active ingredients consisted of various tryptamine derivatives, especially DMT, 5-MeO-DMT and bufotenine (Holmstedt [55] and Fish [25]). "These and related indolealkylamines have been detected in members of at least five different plant families" (Nichols [81], p. 120).

Plant tryptamines are also used by Amazonian shamans in the form of ayahuasca, a dark liquid formed by boiling sections of a vine from the *Banisteriopsis* genus, usually *B. caapi* (Rivier [88]). This vine contains harmala alkaloids, in particular, harmine and harmaline, which are sufficient in themselves to induce visions. Usually another plant is added to the brew "to make the visions more intense" (according to the native shamans). This additional plant is often *Psychotria viridis*, a plant which contains DMT and 5-MeO-DMT. Although the DMT content of ayahuasca is sometimes thought to derive solely from the additives, Stafford [108] reports that the leaves and stems of one species of *Banisteriopsis, B. rusbyana,* "have a large amount of N,N-DMT, 5-methoxy-N,N-DMT, 5-hydroxy-N, N-DMT [bufotenine] and N-β-methyltetra-hydro-β-carboline." DMT is not by itself orally active (in doses of up to one gram), since it is broken down in the gut by the enzyme monoamine oxidase (MAO). This breakdown may be prevented by the presence of an MAO inhibitor, allowing the DMT to enter the blood and reach the brain. Ayahuasca contains an MAO-inhibitor, namely, the β-carbolines derived from the *B. caapi* vine.

Ayahuasca is frequently consumed at night by a group of people (Kensinger [60] and McKenna [69]), although there are large variations in its mode of usage among the Indian tribes of the Amazon. Currently the use of ayahuasca among Indians in the Amazon is declining due to the destruction of traditional tribal cultures. This lends an urgency to the preservation of the knowledge associated with its use, a knowledge which concerns not only the preparation and use of ayahuasca but also the manner in which the experiences of the practitioner are to be interpreted.

In Brazil there is an interesting religious organization known as *Santo daime* whose members use ayahuasca within a Catholic/Christian context. (Richman [87])

(b) Professional and academic research

Stafford [108] mentions that DMT was first synthesized in 1931 by the British chemist Richard Manske (who was also the first to synthesize harmaline, in 1927), and that "Albert Hofmann synthesized a series of DMT analogs, but little attention was paid to this work until the mid-1960s."

In the 1950s and 60s some researchers experimented with tryptamine hallucinogens injected intramuscularly. The first to publish in English on this subject seems to have been the Hungarian investigator Stephen Szara, while working for the U.S. National Institute of Mental Health in Washington, DC. (For some reason most of the earliest researchers appear to have been Hungarians.) Szara published on DMT as early as 1956, and produced a series of at least 11 papers on the pharmacology of the Alkylated tryptamines during the next 11 years. Writing in 1961 he said:

> I became interested in the possibility of hallucinogenic action of alkylated tryptamine derivatives in 1955, when I read about the chemical analysis of a snuff powder prepared by Haitian natives from Piptadenia Peregrina seeds which they used in

[religious ceremonies to produce mystical states of mind which enabled them to communicate with their gods...C]hemical analysis...revealed the presence of bufotenin and a small amount of N,N-dimethyltryptamine (DMT). (Szara [114].)

Szara administered 75 mg of DMT intramuscularly to himself and experienced intense visions. He established "that intramuscular injection of 50 to 60 mg of DMT brought about intense visual displays...within five minutes. These reached peak effects within a quarter of an hour, diminishing and then disappearing totally within half an hour...Subjects became catatonic or lost consciousness when given doses larger than 125 mg." (Stafford [108], p. 314)

During the early 1960s the Southern California psychiatrist Oscar Janiger administered DMT to many subjects. The data and conclusions from these studies remain unpublished. One time he administered to himself an excessive dose and described the result as "terrible—like being inside a gigantic pinball machine with lights going on and off everywhere" [58].

(c) Amateur and extra-mural research

In the 1950s William Burroughs and Allen Ginsberg journeyed to South America in search of the ayahuasca experience. They wrote about this in *The Yagé Letters* [14]. Later Burroughs, like Janiger, injected an overdose (100 mg) of synthetic DMT and had a "horrible experience."

Timothy Leary heard of DMT from Allen Ginsberg and contacted Burroughs, who warned him of the perils of this substance. Undaunted, Leary, Richard Alpert and Ralph Metzner began to experiment, and discovered that the DMT experience, although intense, was manageable and *very* interesting. Leary published in 1966 an article discussing DMT and giving, in his usual style, an extremely positive account of what he experienced following an i.m. injection of 60 mg ([63]).

Stafford writes:

This article by Leary and Metzner caused a wave of interest in DMT among many in the counterculture. About this time came the discovery that DMT evaporated onto oregano, parsley leaves or marijuana and then smoked could produce effects similar to those from injections, except that they occurred almost immediately and disappeared more rapidly. ([108]. p. 315).

There is a certain art to smoking DMT to produce a significant effect which is only acquired with practice. Some who have tried it have not experienced its full effect; others have found it too much to handle. It is indeed not a drug for "party trippers," but only for those who "take drugs seriously." Smoking DMT has been compared by some novice tokers to parachuting at night into the midst of a tribe of frenzied New Guinea natives at the height of an elaborate war-dance.

Carlos Castaneda gives an account of his terrifying experience with something that (apparently in December 1963) Don Juan gave him to smoke ([15], pp. 151–157). Although Castaneda does not identify the substance, one cannot help but wonder whether it contained a psychedelic tryptamine.

[Castaneda:] "But what does the smoke teach, then?"
[Don Juan:] "It shows you how to handle its power, and to learn that you must take it as many times as you can."
[Castaneda:] "Your ally is very frightening, Don Juan. It was unlike anything I ever experienced before. I thought I had lost my mind."
...Don Juan discarded my simile, saying that what I felt was

its unimaginable power. And to handle that power, he said, one has to live a strong life... He said that smoke is so strong one can match it only with strength; otherwise one's life would be shattered to bits. ([15], pp. 160-161).

3. Dosage and duration of effects

In its pure form DMT is a white powder. If it has not been completely purified during the synthetic process it may be encountered as a pale orange waxy material. Dose levels mentioned in this article refer to pure DMT unless otherwise noted.

The amount of DMT needed to produce significant psychic effects when smoked is 5 mg to 20 mg, there being considerable variation in individual reaction. Some people have had "profound" effects with as little as 10 mg. A moderate dose is 20–25 mg, with 40–50 mg a large dose. A very large dose (e.g., 75 mg) will normally lead to loss of consciousness.

Stafford writes of DMT, DET (diethyltryptamine) and DPT (dipropyltryptamine) that "More often [compared to injection], these tryptamines are smoked because less is needed to feel the effects... The DMT peak lasts for three to ten minutes, and it's all over in twenty to thirty minutes. DET and DMT, which have more subtle effects than DMT, may take a few minutes to register... DET lasts about an hour when smoked; the most intense part of a DPT experience is over in about twenty minutes." ([108], p. 322).

Several different methods may be used to smoke DMT, and there are differences of opinion as to their efficiency. "Some users prefer to smoke a compound like DMT... in a small glass pipe. A small amount of the crystals or oil is placed in the bowl and then slowly heated until fumes begin to fill the pipe... A regular pipe covered with a fine screen can be used." (Stafford [108]). In this method the DMT should be spread over some plant material such as mint leaves, parsley, marijuana or mullein (which is smoked by asthmatics to clear bronchial passages); a flame is held over the bowl and the vaporized DMT is inhaled deeply. It is usually advisable to do this under the guidance of a person who is experienced in this practice.

When smoked, one or two deep inhalations may be sufficient in the case of some people to cause profound effects very quickly, whereas others may require up to four or five inhalations for full effect. One should be in a position to lie or to lean back comfortably, since the effects of smoking a large amount (e.g., 30–40 mg) are usually physically incapacitating. Some favor a sitting position. As noted above, the effect is more intense in the first few minutes, and mostly wears off after about ten minutes. Since DMT occurs naturally in the human brain there are probably homeostatic mechanisms for regulating the concentration of DMT, which would explain the rapidity with which the effects wear off.

DMT has been extensively tested both in the U.S. and in Europe and is apparently quite safe in normal subjects. The only case of a severely adverse reaction which has been reported in the literature is that of a woman who received 40 mg intramuscularly and who "suddenly developed an extremely rapid heart rate 12 minutes after the injection; no pulse could be obtained; no blood pressure could be measured. There seemed to have been an onset of auricular fibrillation." (Turner [126], p. 127). However, this woman was schizophrenic and at the time of the injection had been extremely tense and apprehensive.

I am informed that to pursue DMT experimentation safely one should have good cardiovascular health and avoid drugs and foods which increase heart rate and blood pressure by direct stimulation of the heart or by vasoconstriction. DMT should not be used by anyone who is taking MAO inhibiting drugs.

4. Subjective effects of smoking DMT

The subjective effects of a good lungful of DMT are usually very intense, with consciousness usually overwhelmed by visual imagery. With eyes closed this may take the form of extremely complex, dynamic, geometric patterns, changing rapidly. Such a dose of DMT may produce a visual pattern consisting of overlapping annual patterns of small rhomboid elements all in saturated hues of red, yellow, green and blue. Gracie & Zarkov [44] refer to this, or something similar, as "the chrysanthemum pattern." The pattern itself seems to be charged with a portentous energy.

The state of consciousness characterized by amazing visual patterns seems to be a prelude to a more profound state, which subjects report as contact with entities described as discarnate, nonhuman or alien. A very articulate account of the subjective effects of smoking DMT is given by Terence McKenna in his talk *Tryptamine Hallucinogens and Consciousness* [72], in which he recounts his contact with what he calls "elves."

As usual with tryptamine psychedelics there is normally no loss of ego, although large doses will produce unconsciousness. There is often loss of body awareness. It is usually possible to think under the influence of DMT, but with larger doses it may become difficult to hold a thought, and sometimes confusion will occur.

With a fully effective dose (e.g., 25 mg), the experience is usually so bizarre that an inexperienced person may believe that he or she has died, or is dying, especially if body awareness is lost. If this belief arises then it is important to remember that one will survive and return to ordinary consciousness. In general, yielding to the temptation to believe that one has died is not helpful when navigating psychedelic states since the resultant anxiety will usually distract one from a scientific observation of what is going on. More experienced users, knowing that hitherto they have always survived, however weird the experience, can learn not to succumb to this anxiety.

5. Personal reports

As regards the nature of the DMT experience, we are still at the Baconian, data-gathering, stage. Before going on to offer some generalizations and speculation I shall here present some descriptions of DMT experiences, especially insofar as they relate to the question of contact with discarnate entities. Because the use of DMT is still illegal in certain countries whose governments do not yet recognize a person's natural right to modify his or her consciousness in whatever way desired, the authors of these reports shall for now remain anonymous.

Subject S (no previous experience with DMT; written communication):

My first attempts with DMT have left me with some serious thoughts... I did less than 10 mg on my second attempt and had a very weird experience. Not only did I have what I can only call a "close encounter," I was left with two thoughts. First, they were waiting for me, and they were not "friendly." ...[On the] third attempt [it] seemed like they could not wait for me to experiment. In this event, I did not have actual contact, but rather "felt" them wanting to get into my con-sciousness. The actual experience was far more frightening than any major "trip" previously experienced.... I was pro-foundly affected.

Subject O (description of first DMT experience; written communication):

Remember to breathe. Recline and get into position, subsumed by the momentum; before me I see an irridescent membrane, taut and gently pulsating, something stretching and pushing towards me, on the other side, straining to emerge. A fissure rends, tears and inside I glimpse the existence of something/ place consisting of a dense whirling body of brilliantly multi-colored primordial life/thought stuff, seeping and beckoning... I breathe and return into the plexus, center of my being, to witness myself as an outline-constructed 2-D diagramatic shell of many coherent light-points, revolving quadrated vortices, large central to smaller and then tiny outer, phos-phorescent green and I... enter into utter emptiness, space matrix.... [I]mpression of basic colors, unmuted blue, yellow and red, shimmering into being, depth imperceptible yet de-fined within the space, endlessly recurring back from/into the corner when, slowly, from around the edges they peer toward me, watching, eyes bright and watching in small faces, then small hands to pull themselves, slowly, from be-hind and into view; they are small white-blond imp-kids, very old in bright, mostly red, togs and caps; candy-store, shiny, teasing and inquisitive, very solemn and somewhat pleased (ah, here you are!) watching me as I meet only their eyes bright and dark without any words (look!) or any idea remembered they only want to convey (look!) through their eyes that I must know that THIS is what they/we are doing...

Subject O (second DMT experience; written communication):

...I found myself once again in the company of the "elves," as the focus of their attention and ministrations, but they appeared much less colorful and altogether preoccupied with the task at hand, i.e., pouring a golden, viscous liquid through a network of long, intertwining, transparent conduits which led into the middle of my abdomen...

Subject G (very experienced with DMT; Gracie [44], #5):

We each had taken 150 mg of pure MDA....About hour 4, I decided to try smoking some DMT....This time I saw the "elves" as multidimensional creatures formed by strands of visible language; they were more creaturely than I had ever seen them before....The elves were dancing in and out of the multidimensional visible language matrix, "waving" their "arms" and "limbs/hands/fingers?" and "smiling" or "laughing," although I saw no faces as such. The elves were "telling" me (or I was understanding them to say) that I had seen them before, in early childhood. Memories were flooding back of seeing the elves: they looked just like they do now: evershifting, folding, multidimensional, multicolored (what colors!), always laughing, weaving/waving, showing me things, showing me the visible language they are created/creatures of, teaching me to speak and read.

Subject T (several previous DMT experiences; verbal communication):

I saw a tunnel, which I flew down at great speed. I approached the end of the tunnel, which was closed by two doors on which was written: THE END. I burst through these and was carried up through seven heavens, breaking through each one in turn. When I emerged at the top I was flying over a dark landscape (it seemed to be Mexico). I felt that this was all so weird that I should be scared (perhaps I had died), but I did not feel scared. I continued to fly on, over a ravine, leading up to a mountainside, and eventually saw a campfire. As I approached this, cautiously, I saw that on the other side of the fire was a human figure wearing a sombrero, whom I intuitively knew to be Don Juan. He invited me to come closer, and spoke to me.

Subject V (very experienced with DMT; verbal communication):

I was in a large space and saw what seemed to be thousands of the entities. They were rapidly passing something to and fro among themselves, and were looking intently at me, as if to say "See what we are doing!"... I noticed what seemed to be an opening into a large space, like looking through a cave opening to a starry sky. As I approached this I saw that resting in the opening was a large creature, with many arms, somewhat like an octopus, and all over the arms were eyes, mostly closed, as if the creature were asleep or slumbering. As I approached it the eyes opened, and it/they became aware of me. It did not seem especially well-disposed towards me, as if it did not wish to be bothered by a mere human, and I had the impression I wasn't going to get past it, so I did not try.

Subject M (several previous DMT experiences: written report; each of the following paragraphs in this section is a description of a separate experience):

(i) It was not until my fifth DMT trip that I became aware of alien contact. I took two inhalations from a mixture of 75 mg of DMT wax (less than 100% pure) and mullein. The visual hallucination was experienced as overwhelming, totally amazing, incredible and unbelievable. I could only surrender to the experience, reminding myself that I would survive, and attempt to deal with the sense that what I was seeing was completely impossible. I wondered whether this was what dying was like, and reassured myself, through noting my breathing, that I was still alive. What I was experiencing was happening too quickly to comprehend. At one point I suddenly became aware of beings, who were rapidly flitting about me. They appeared as dark, stick-like beings silhouetted against a rapidly-changing kaleidoscopic background. Although I could not make out much detail, I definitely felt their presence.

(ii) On the sixth occasion I took two inhalations of about 35 mg of pure DMT in a glass pipe. Immediately upon closing my eyes I was overwhelmed by visual hallucination. This seemed to last but briefly, whereupon I passed abruptly through to another realm, losing all awareness of my body. It was as if there were alien beings there waiting for me, and I recall that they spoke to me as if they had been awaiting my arrival, but I cannot remember exactly what was said. This time, rather than (or as well as) flitting about me, the entities

approached me from the front, rapidly and repeatedly, appearing to enter and pass through me. I could make no sense of what was happening. I opened my eyes and made contact with my companions, locating myself once more in the room from which I had begun. Immediately I completely forgot what I had just experienced. The contents of the room appeared stable but weirdly distorted. I was able to recognize and to talk to my companions, but I felt and appeared very disoriented. . . . The memory of this experience came back only when, later that evening, I smoked the remainder of what was left in the pipe—not enough to break through, but enough for me to remember. . . .

(iii) . . . I got deeply into the visual hallucination. I was barely able to remind and to reassure myself that "DMT is safe," though I had some difficulty recalling the name "DMT." With eyes closed, I experienced intense, overwhelming visual imagery. I was seeing a large, extremely colorful surface, like a membrane, pulsating toward and away from me. . . . I recalled that I had seen this before, on previous DMT trips, but had forgotten it. During this experience I was aware of my breathing and heartbeat, and was careful to continue breathing deeply. The pattern was in intense hues, and its parts seemed to have meaning, as if they were letters of an alphabet, but I could not make sense of it. I was quite amazed. I felt that I was being shown something, and I tried to understand what I was seeing, but could not. I also heard elf-language, but it was not meaningful to me. Eventually the visions subsided, with no breakthrough and no overt alien contact.

(iv) I smoked at around 2 a.m. with little effect and some vaguely unpleasant visual hallucination (harlequin-like gargoyles?). This might have been due to being tired and to having eaten substantially a few hours before. There was a sense of alien presence. Upon awakening next morning I

noticed that my electronic alarm clock, while obviously still "ticking," had stopped at the time I had been smoking the previous night. I have never known the clock to stop in this way before or since.

(v) Smoked 40–50 mg of DMT wax. . . . An overwhelming and confusing experience. My heart rate seemed to go way up, which caused me some concern. I had to remind myself that one does not die from smoking DMT. The experience was disjointed and erratic. There were white flashes, like subtitles in a film, except that they were not verbal but rather like a white-energy-being rushing quickly through the scene from left to right (what I now think of as "the white lightning being"). There was a strange, incomprehensible auditory hallucination. Confusing and unpleasant. I reflected that this is what hell might be like (good practice for hell: stay calm and try to observe what is happening).

(vi) Upon lying back I became aware of brightly colored, moving patterns, which I remembered having seen before on DMT (but having forgotten about—indeed even now, a half-hour later, I cannot recall them clearly). I was then immersed in a totally weird state, like being in a large multicolored hall whose walls (if it had walls) were moving incomprehensibly. . . . Apart from occasional awareness of my breathing I was hardly aware of my body at all. I seemed to be in another world, disembodied, and feeling flabbergasted. I seemed to be aware of the presence of other beings in the same space, but had only fleeting glimpses of them, as if they were shy about appearing to me. In this state I did not know what to do. It was as if I was offered a wish by the dragon but did not understand what was being offered—or even that there was a dragon at all. Throughout there was elf-music, and elf-language in the background. I did not attend much to this since the visual effects were so overwhelming. As the influence of the DMT wore off I felt myself losing contact with

this state, and I knew that I would forget what was happening. It felt as if there were beings "waving goodbye."

(vii) I smoked 40 mg of pure DMT mixed with some marijuana....I quickly entered into the trance state without noticing any great amount of the usual patterned visual hallucination....I seemed to be falling away, spiraling into some large, black void, after which I seemed to be in a bright, open space in the presence of two other beings. Their forms were not very clear, but they seemed to be like children, as if we were together in a playground. They appeared to be moving very rapidly....The two beings seemed to be trying to attract my attention, and to communicate something to me, but I could not understand. It was as if they were trying to make me understand where I was. One even seemed to be holding up a sign, like a speech balloon, but, as I recall, the sign was blank. I attended to my breathing, and with this came an increased sense of self-identity, and with this a lessening of contact with the two beings.

(viii) Smoked 40 mg spread over mint leaves, in three tokes, sitting upright. My intention was to see what spirits, if any, are currently about me. As the experience came upon me I managed to keep that intention, or at least, "What spirits...?" and also remembered to breathe regularly. A strange state of mind ensued, one of dynamic, patterned energy, in which I was not sure whether I was perceiving a scene, with a moving being, or not. I finally realized that the answer to my question regarding spirits was that there were indeed many around me, and that they were merry, hiding and playing a joke on me. However, I did not specifically see or hear any.

(ix) Smoked 40 mg of DMT wax spread over mint leaves as usual, sitting up leaning against a pillow....As the trance came on I was overwhelmed with visual imagery that I did not even attempt to make sense of. I struggled to remember who I was....[I] turned my attention to the visual compo-

nent, and what I saw was an incredible amount of stuff coming at me in waves, sort of rolling toward me. There were two beings in the scene, and they were doing the rolling, definitely throwing all this stuff at me—I don't know why. The scene changed, and there was more visual hallucination, but I don't remember the details—all happening very quickly.

6. Levels of experience

Based upon these reports and others I tentatively put forward the following classification of levels of experience associated with the effects of smoking DMT. This classification should be tested in the light of further reports, in particular those resulting from an experiment currently being conducted involving the administration of DMT via i.v. injection to about a dozen subjects. (Strassman [111]).

Level I: Pre-hallucinatory experience.

This stage is characterized by an interior flowing of energy/consciousness. It may be extremely intense. It may have a positive feeling content.

Level II: Vivid, brilliantly colored, geometric visual hallucinations.

Here one is observing a patterned field, basically two-dimensional, although it may have a pulsating quality. One may remember having seen this before.

Transitional Phase (Level IIB?): tunnel or breakthrough experience.

One may see or fly through a tunnel (a passage to the next level). A veil may part, a membrane may be rent. There is a breakthrough to another world (or perhaps even a series of breakthroughs).

Alternatively, it may also happen that the transition from Level II to Level III is abrupt, almost instantaneous, with no experience of transition.

Level III: Three- or higher-dimensional space, possible contact with entities.

This stage is characterized by the experience of being in an "objective" space, that is, a space of at least three dimensions in which objects or entities may be encountered. Sometimes the entities appear to be intelligent and communicating beings. This stage may be extremely energetic with an experience of everything happening incomprehensibly fast. Alternatively it may be relatively coherent.

Travel is possible at Level III. One may, for example, assume the form and consciousness of a bird, and fly as a bird does (cf. Castaneda [15], pp. 191–196). The limits of this stage, if any, are unknown. There may be transitions to further stages.

7. Interpretations of the experience

Although the amazing geometrical visual hallucinations experienced under the influence of DMT are sufficient in themselves to command attention among students of psychedelics, the really interesting part of the experience is the apparent contact with alien beings. Since some may feel reluctant to admit the possible existence of alien beings getting in contact with DMT-modified humans, we should consider all hypotheses that might explain the observations, or at least, be consistent with them.

Several questions can be distinguished. Firstly, there is the question of the independent reality of the entities. Subjects report experiences of contact with communicating beings whose independent existence at the time seems self-evident. These experiences are not described as dream-like. If the entities have an existence independent of the DMT-influenced subject, then a realm of existence has been discovered which is quite other than the consensus reality which most of us assume is the only real world.

Such a discovery of "a separate reality" would directly challenge the foundations of the modern Western view of the world. I was tempted to say that it would be the most revolutionary change in our understanding of reality since the fish crawled out on land, but this would be overlooking the fact that the world view of the modern West is a comparatively recent invention, stemming mainly from the rise of materialist science in recent centuries. Earlier cultures had, and non-Western cultures still have, more expansive views of the extent of reality.

Secondly, regardless of whether the entities are independently-existing or have no existence beyond the experience of the subject, what are they seen as and seen to be doing? What is happening, for example, when some subjects (e.g., Subject V) report seeing thousands of these entities simultaneously? Even more interesting is the phenomenon of communication, or attempted communication, which many subjects report (e.g., Subjects O, G, T and M). Some subjects also report seeing the entities communicating with each other, in some kind of mutual exchange—but of what?

Thirdly, the matter can be approached from the point of view of neuropharmacology. What exactly is going on when those DMT molecules get in there among the neurons of the brain, causing it to function in what appears subjectively to be a radically different manner?

Listed below are eight suggested interpretations of the DMT experience which imply answers (true or false) to some or all of the questions raised above. Some of these, like the experience itself, are bizarre, but at this stage any idea should be considered since in this matter the truth (to paraphrase J.B.S. Haldane) probably is not only stranger than we suppose but stranger than we *can* suppose.

(i) There are no alien entities at all; it's merely subjective hallucination. The DMT state may be interesting, even extremely interesting, but really there are no independently-existing alien entities to be found.

(ii) DMT provides access to a parallel or higher dimension, a truly alternate reality which is, in fact, inhabited by independently-existing intelligent entities forming (in the words of Terence McKenna) "an ecology of souls."

(iii) DMT allows awareness of processes at a cellular or even atomic level. DMT smokers are tapping into the network of cells in the brain or even into communication among molecules themselves. It might even be an awareness of quantum mechanical processes at the atomic or subatomic level.

(iv) DMT is, perhaps, a neurotransmitter in reptilian brains and in the older, reptilian parts of mammalian brains. Flooding the human brain with DMT causes the older reptilian parts of the brain to dominate consciousness, resulting in a state of awareness which appears totally alien (and sometimes very frightening) to the everyday monkey mind.

(v) A non-human intelligent species created humans by genetic modification of existing primate stock then retreated, leaving behind biochemical methods for contacting them. The psychedelic tryptamines are chemical keys that activate certain programs in the human brain that were placed there intentionally by this alien species.

(vi) The realm to which DMT provides access is the world

of the dead. The entities experienced are the souls, or personalities, of the departed, which retain some kind of life and ability to communicate. The realm of dead souls, commonly accepted by cultures and societies other than that of the modern West, is now accessible using DMT.

(vii) The entities experienced are beings from another time who have succeeded in mastering the art of time travel, not in a way which allows materialization but in a way which allows them to communicate with conscious beings such as ourselves.

(viii) The entities are probes from an extraterrestrial or an extradimensional species, sent out to make contact with organisms such as ourselves who are able to manipulate their nervous systems in a way which allows communication to take place.

These hypotheses can be expanded and are, of course, vulnerable to objections. No doubt other hypotheses are possible. These matters will not be resolved until we have more data with which to test these and other hypotheses.

8. DMT and hyperspace

In this section and the following one I shall present a view which elaborates upon interpretations (ii), (vi) and (vii). This is speculation but nevertheless provides a preliminary framework for steps toward an understanding of what the use of DMT reveals to us.

The world of ordinary, common, experience has three spatial dimensions and one temporal dimension, forming a place and time for the apparent persistence of solid objects. Since this is a world of experience it belongs more to experience than to being. The being, or ontological nature, of this world may be quite different from what we experience it as.

Psychedelic experience strongly suggests that (as William James hypothesized) ordinary experience is an island in a sea of possible modes of consciousness. Under the influence of substances such as LSD and psilocybin we venture outside of the world as commonly viewed and enter spaces which may be very strange indeed. This happens as a result of changing our brain chemistry. Why then should we not regard ordinary experience too as a result of a particular mode of brain chemistry? Perhaps the world of ordinary experience is not a faithful representation of physical reality but rather is physical reality represented in the manner of ordinary brain functioning. By taking this idea seriously we may free our understanding of physical reality from the limitations imposed by the unthinking assumption that ordinary experience represents physical reality as it is. In fact physical reality may be totally bizarre and quite unlike anything we have thought it to be.

In his special theory of relativity, Albert Einstein demonstrated that the physical world (the world that can be measured by physical instruments, but is assumed to exist independently) is best understood as a four-dimensional space which may be separated into three spatial dimensions and one temporal dimension in various ways, the particular separation depending on the motion of a hypothetical observer. It seems that DMT releases one's consciousness from the ordinary experience of space and time and catapults one into direct experience of a four-dimensional world. This explains the feeling of incredulity which first-time users frequently report.

The DMT realm is described by some as "incredible," "bizarre," "unbelievable" and even "impossible," and for many who have experienced it these terms are not an exaggeration. These terms make sense if the world experienced under DMT is a four-dimensional world experienced by a mind which is trying to make sense of it in terms of its usual categories of three-dimensional space and one-dimensional time. In the DMT state these categories no longer apply to whatever it is that is being experienced.

Some persons report that it seems that in the DMT experience there is information transfer of some sort. If so, and if this information is quite unlike anything that we are used to dealing with (at least at a conscious level), then it may be that the bizarre quality of the experience results from attempting to impose categories of thought which are quite inapplicable.

The space that one breaks through to under the influence of a large dose of DMT has been called "hyperspace" by Terence McKenna and Ralph Abraham [74] and by Gracie & Zarkov [44]. I suggest that hyperspace is an experience of physical reality which is "closer" to it (or less mediated) than is our ordinary experience. In hyperspace one has direct experience of the four-dimensionality of physical reality.

Parenthetically we may note a mildly interesting case of historical anticipation. In 1897 one H.C. Geppinger published a book entitled *DMT: Dimensional Motion Times* [31], an appropriate title for our current subject. However, he was, of course, quite unaware of what the initials "DMT" would later come to mean.

When reflecting upon his mescaline experiences Aldous Huxley suggested that there was something, which he called "Mind-at-Large," which was filtered by the ordinary functioning of the human brain to produce ordinary experience. One may view the human body and the human nervous system as a cybernetic system for constructing a stable representation of a world of enduring objects which are able to interact in ways that we are familiar with from our ordinary experience. This is analogous to a computer's production of a stable video display—for even a simple blinking cursor requires complicated coordination of underlying physical processes to make it happen. In a sense we are (or at least we may be thought of as) biological computers whose typical output is the world of everyday reality (as we experience it). When our biocomputational processes are modified by strange chemicals we have the opportunity to view the reality underlying ordinary experience in an entirely new way.

Einstein's four-dimensional space-time may thus turn out to be not merely a flux of energetic point-events but to be (or to be contained in a higher-dimensional space which is) at least as organized as our ordinary world and which contains intelligent, communicating beings capable of interacting with us. As Hamlet remarked to his Aristotelian tutor, following an encounter with a dead soul (his deceased father), "There are more things in heaven and earth, Horatio, than are dreamt of in your philosophy." Should we be surprised to find that there are more intelligent, communicating, beings in the higher-dimensional reality underlying our ordinary experience than we find within that experience?

9. The "elves"

Hyperspace, as it is revealed by DMT (revealed to some, anyway) appears to be full of personal entities. They are non-physical in the sense that they are not objects in the three-dimensional space to which we are accustomed. Some of the beings encountered in the DMT state may once have been living humans, but perhaps such "dead souls" are in the minority among the intelligent beings in that realm.

In his classic *The Fairy Faith in Celtic Countries* [21], W.Y. Evans-Wentz recorded many tales provided to him by local people of encounters with beings, variously called fairies, elves, the wee folk, the good people, the gentry, the *Sidhe*, the Tuatha De Danann, etc., who inhabit a realm normally beyond our ken. The belief in this order of beings was firm among the Celtic peoples of Britain and France at the time Evans-Wentz conducted his studies (c. 1900), but has since been largely supplanted by the beliefs instilled in the public by the rise of materialistic science and technology. Evans-Wentz collected numerous reports of elf-sightings, such as the following (which is part of an account given by a member of the Lower House of the Manx Parliament):

> ...I looked across the river and saw a circle of supernatural light, which I have now come to regard as the "astral light" or the light of Nature, as it is called by mystics, and in which spirits become visible...[I]nto this space, and the circle of light, from the surrounding sides apparently, I saw come in twos and threes a great crowd of little beings smaller than Tom Thumb and his wife. All of them, who appeared like soldiers, were dressed in red. They moved back and forth amid the circle of light, as they formed into order like troops drilling. ([21], p. 113)

Reviewing his data, Evans-Wentz writes:

> We seem, in fact, to have arrived at a point in our long investigations where we can postulate scientifically, on the showing of the data of psychical research, the existence of such invisible intelligences as gods, genii, daemons, all kinds of true fairies, and disembodied [i.e., deceased]men. ([21], p. 481)

He then goes on to quote an earlier researcher:

> Either it is we who produce these phenomena [which, says Evans-Wentz, is unreasonable] or it is spirits. But mark this

well: these spirits are not necessarily the souls of the dead; for other kinds of spiritual beings may exist, and space may be full of them without our ever knowing anything about it, except under unusual circumstances [such as a sudden change in brain chemistry]. Do we not find in the different ancient literatures, demons, angels, gnomes, goblins, sprites, spectres, elementals, etc.? Perhaps these legends are not without some foundation in fact. (Flammarion [28], quoted in [21], p. 481)

Evans-Wentz concludes ([21], p. 490) that a realm of discarnate, intelligent forces known as fairies, elves, etc., exists "as a supernormal state of consciousness into which men and women may enter temporarily in dreams, trances, or in various ecstatic conditions," such as, we may add, the condition produced by smoking DMT.

I suggest that the faerie world studied by Evans-Wentz and the objective space into which one may enter under the influence of DMT are the same.

10. DMT and the death state

Who are we and how did we get here? Clearly we are personalities who develop in connection with our bodies. But are we personalities who have our origin in the development of our bodies? Or do we originate as hyperspatial entities who become associated with bodies for the purpose of acting in what appears to us as the ordinary world? The answer may be a combination of both. It may be that a personality must first come into existence in connection with a body but that, once developed, it may leave the body, and perhaps subsequently become associated with a new body. Or it may be that intelligent entities, most of whom were never human, can come into existence as beings in hyperspace by virtue of a creative power associated with the origin of hyperspace itself. In the more poetic words of an Irish seer, they may "draw their life out of the Soul of the World" ([21], p. 65).

DMT appears to allow us to leave our three-dimensional bodily organisms and enter into hyperspace where we can function (for a short period of earthly time while our brain biochemistry is altered) as disembodied personalities, able to communicate with other discarnate personalities. In fact it may be that this is what happens to us when we die. In death, however, unlike the DMT trance, you can't return to your body. Once your body is destroyed, or is damaged so that it cannot function as a channel for your will, then you have entered hyperspace and you will remain there indefinitely or until association with a new body becomes possible.

After telling of frequently seeing spiritual beings enveloped in shining light, one of Evan-Wentz's informants says:

In whatever country we may be, I believe that we are for ever immersed in the spiritual world; but most of us cannot perceive it on account of the unrefined nature of our physical bodies. Through meditation and psychical training one can come to see the spiritual world and its beings. We pass into the spirit realm at death and come back into the human world at birth; and we continue to reincarnate until we have overcome all earthly desires and mortal appetites. Then the higher life is open to our consciousness and we cease to be human; we become divine beings. ([21], p. 84)

It now seems possible, by the use of the psychedelic tryptamines, to venture into the death state before we die and to accustom ourselves to that state. This is the path of the shaman and the spiritual warrior. At death, when the transition is finally and irrevocably made, the psychedelic explorer will enter a realm he or she knows from previous experience, and will, hopefully, not be swept away by fear and ignorance.

11. Further research needed

The idea that there might be a realm inhabited by alien beings able to communicate with humans in an intelligent manner, and that these beings may be contacted through the use of a psychedelic, is sufficiently bizarre that some may be tempted to reject it unthinkingly. Modern-day common sense certainly rejects the possibility entirely, but a scientific approach to the subject requires suspension of common sense in favor of an unbiased study of the available data. In this case the rawest data available is the actual subjective experience of the DMT state.

Further research is needed to distinguish among the possible interpretations presented above, or to provide a basis for other interpretations. Basically this means further human explorations of the DMT experience, with articulate reports on the experience. This would allow us to begin to determine what are the common characteristics, in humans, of the experienced induced by smoking DMT. Do all subjects eventually experience (apparent) contact with alien beings? How is this contact related to dose and method of administration? In what form(s) do the entities (tend to) appear? How often are cases of human-alien communication reported? What is the content of this communication?

As an aid to further research in this field I have compiled the bibliography of publications, mostly articles concerning DMT, which is reproduced below.

Contact with alien entities in other worlds has long been reported from non-Western and pre-modern societies. Such reports are usually presented in the context of a particular mythology or cosmology that makes it difficult to relate them to a modern scientific view of the world. This may mean not that these reports are false, but that our scientific view of the world needs to be extended. A scientific attitude—that is, an open and questioning attitude to the advancement of knowledge, one which does not shun any repeatable observation regardless of how bizarre it may seem—is not inconsistent with the discovery of intelligent, non-human entities in a higher-dimensional realm. If they are there, and can be contacted reliably, let us see what they have to say.

Acknowledgments

I would like to thank those people (you know who you are) who read earlier drafts of this article (it was begun in October 1989 and completed in June 1991) and who offered helpful criticism and suggestions for improvement.

Bibliography

[1] Arnold, O.H., and Hofmann, G.: "Zur Psychopathologie des Dimethyl-tryptamin: ein weiterer Beitrag Zur Pharmakopsychiatrie," *Wein. Zeitschr. Nervenh.,* 13 (1957), pp. 438-445.

[2] Axelrod, J.: "Enzymatic formation of psychotomimetic metabolites from normally occurring compounds," *Science,* 134 (1961), p. 343.

[3] Axelrod, J.: "The enzymatic N-methylation of serotonin and other amines," *J. Clin. Endrocrinol. Metab.,* 61 (1962), pp. 388-390.

[4] Barker, S.A., Monti, J.A., and Christian, S.T.: "N,N-

Dimethyltryptamine: an Endogenous Hallucinogen," *International Review of Neurobiology,* 22 (1981), pp. 83-110.

[5] Beaton, J., and Morris, P.: "Ontogeny of N,N-dimethyltryptamine and related indolealkylamine levels in neonatal rats," *Mech. Age. Develop.,* 25, pp. 343-347.

[6] Benington, F., Morin, R.D., and Clark, L.C.: "5-Methoxy-N,N-dimethyltryptamine, a possible endogenous psychotoxin," *Ala. J. Med. Sci.,* 2 (1965), pp. 397-403.

[7] Bickel, P., Dittrich, A., and Schoepf, J.: "Eine experimentelle Untersuchung zur bewusstseinverandenden Wirkung von N,N-Dimethyl-tryptamine (DMT)," *Pharmakopsychiatr. Neuropsychopharmakol.,* 9 (1976), pp. 220-225.

[8] Borsey, J., Lénárd, K., and Csizmadia, Zs.: "Über die zentrale Wirkung von Diäthyltryptamine und seiner an 2. Stelle substituierten aromatischen Derivative im Zusammenhang mit den Mediatorsubstanzen der autonomen Zentren," *Acta Physiol. Acad. Sci. Hung.,* 18 (1961), pp. 83-84.

[9] Boszormenyi, Z., Der, P., and Nagy, T.: "Observations on the psychotogenic effect of N,N-diethyltryptamine, a new tryptamine derivative," *J. Ment. Sci.,* 105 (1959), pp. 171-181.

[10] Bradley, P. B., Deniker, P., and Radouco-Thomas, C. (eds.): *Neuropsychopharmacology*, Elsevier, 1959.

[11] ———, Flügel, F., and Hoch, P.H. (eds.): *Neuropharmacology,* Vol. III, Proceedings of the Third Meeting of the Collegium Internationale Neuro-Psychopharmacologicum, Elsevier, 1964.

[12] Brimblecombe and Pinder: *Hallucinogenic Agents.*

[13] Brune, G.B., and Pscheidt, G.R.: "Correlations between behavior and urinary excretion of indole amines and catecholamines in schizophrenic patients as affected by drugs," *Federation Proc.,* 20, No. 4 (December 1961), pp. 889-893.

[14] Burroughs, W.S., and Ginsberg, A.: *The Yagé Letters,* City Lights Books, 1988.

[15] Castaneda, C.: *The Teachings of Don Juan: A Yaqui Way of Knowledge,* Touchstone, 1968.

[16] Cerletti, A., Taeschler, M., and Weidmann, H.: "Pharmacologic studies on the structure-activity relationship of hydroxyindole alkylamines," *Adv. Pharmacol. Chemother.,* 6B (1968), pp. 233-246.

[17] Christian S.T., et al.: "The *in Vitro* Identification of Dimethyltryptamine (DMT) in Mammalian Brain and its Characterization as a Possible Endogenous Neuroregulatory Agent," *Biochemical Medicine,* 18 (1977), pp. 164-183.

[18] Corbett, L., et al.: *British Journal of Psychiatry* 132 (1978), pp. 139-144.

[19] Cottrell A., McLeod, M., and McLeod, W.: "A bufotenin-like substance in the urine of schizophrenics," *Am. J. Psychiatry,* 134, pp. 322-323.

[20] DeMontigny, C., and Aghajanian, G.: "Preferential action of 5-methoxy-tryptamine and 5-methoxy-dimethyltryptamine on presynaptic serotonin receptors: A comparative iontophoretic study with LSD and serotonin," *Neuropharmacology,* 77 (1977), pp. 811-818.

[21] Evans-Wentz, W.Y.: *The Fairy Faith in Celtic Countries* (introduction by T. McKenna), Citadel Press, 1990.

[22] Fabing, H.D.: "On going berserk: a neurochemical inquiry," *Am. J. Psychiat.,* 113 (1956), pp. 409-415.

[23] —— and Hawkins, J.R.: "Intravenous bufotenine injection in the human being," *Science,* 123 (1956), pp. 885-887.

[24] —— et al.: "Bufotenine effects in humans," *Fed. Proc.,* 15 (1956), p. 421.

[25] Fish, M.S., Johnson, N.M., and Horning, E.C.: *J. Am. Chem. Soc.,* 77 (1955), p. 5892.

[26] —— and Horning, E.C.: "Studies on Hallucinogenic Snuffs," *J. Nerv. & Ment. Dis.,* 124 (1956). pp. 33-37.

[27] Fisher, G.: "Some Comments Concerning Dosage Lev-

els of Psychedelic Compounds for Psychotherapeutic Experiences," *Psychedelic Review*, 2 (Fall 1963), pp. 208-218.

[28] Flammarion, C.: *Mysterious Psychic Forces,* Boston, 1907.

[29] Freedman, D.X.: "Aspects of the Biochemical Pharmacology of Psychotropic Drugs," *Psychedelic Review,* 8 (1966), pp. 33-58. Reprinted from Solomon [105].

[30] Garattini, S., and Ghetti, V. (eds.): *Psychotropic Drugs,* Elsevier, 1957.

[31] Geppinger, H.C.: *DMT: Dimensional Motion Times, Development and Application* (1897), reprinted Wiley, 1955).

[32] Gessner, P.K., McIsaac, W.M., and Page, I.H.: "Pharmacological actions of some methoxyindolealkylamines," *Nature*, 190 (1961), pp. 179-180.

[33] —— et al.: "The relation between the metabolic fate and pharmacological actions of serotonin, bufotenine and psilocybin," *J. Pharmacol. Exp. Therap.,* 130 (1960), pp. 126-133.

[34] —— and Page, I.H.: "Behavioral effects of 5-methoxy-N,N-dimethyltryptamine, other tryptamines, and LSD," *Am. J. Physiol.,* 203 (1962), pp. 167-172.

[35] —— and Dankova, J.: "Brain bufotenine from administered acetylbufotenine: Comparison of its tremorigenic activity with that of N,N-dimethyltryptamine and 5-methoxyN,N-dimethyltryptamine," *Pharmacologist,* 17 (1975), p. 259.

[36] Giarman, N.J.: Discussion of Kety [61], *Federation Proc.,* Vol. 20, No. 4 (December 1961), pp. 897-900.

[37] Gillin, J., et al.: "The psychedelic model of schizophrenia: The case of N, N-dimethyltryptamine," *Am. J. Psychiatry,* 133 (1976), pp. 203-208.

[38] ——, Stoff, D.M., and Wyatt, R.J.: "Transmethylation hypothesis: A review of progress," in [64], pp. 1097-1112.

[39] —— et al.: "5-methoxy-N,N-dimethyltryptamine:

Behavioral and toxicological effects in animals," *Biol. Psychiatry,* 11 (1976), pp. 355-358.

[40] Glennon, R.A., Liebowitz, S.M., and Mack, E.C.: "Serotonin receptor binding affinities of several hallucinogenic phenylalkylamine and N,N-dimethyltryptamine analogues," *J. Med. Chem.,* 21 (1978), pp. 822-825.

[41] ——— et al.: "Bufotenine esters," *J. Med. Chem.,* 22 (1979), pp. 1414-1416.

[42] ———, Young, R., and Jacyno, J.A.: "Indolealkylamine and phenylalkylamine hallucinogens. Effect of alpha-methyl and N-methyl substituents on behavioural activity," *Biochem. Pharmac.,* 32 (1983), pp. 1267-1273.

[43] ———, Titeler, M., and McKenney, J.: "Evidence for 5HT2 involvement in the mechanism of action of hallucinogenic agents," *Life Sci.* 35 (1984), pp. 2505-2511.

[44] Gracie & Zarkov, *Notes from Underground,* privately printed, 1985.

[45] Granier-Doyeux, M.: "Una Toxicomania Indígena: El Uso de la *Piptadenia peregrina,*" *Revista Técnica,* 2 (1956), pp. 49-55.

[46] Gucchait, R: "Biogenesis of 5-methoxy-N,N-dimethyltryptamine in human pineal gland," *J. Neurochem.,* 26 (1976), pp. 187-190.

[47] Guenter, G.B., and Pscheidt, G.R.: "Correlations between behavior and urinary excretion of indole amines and catecholamines in schizophrenic patients as affected by drugs," *Feder. Proc.,* 20 (1961), pp. 889-893.

[48] Harner. M. (ed.): *Hallucinogens and Shamanism,* Oxford University Press, 1973.

[49] Hartley, R., and Smith, J.: "The activation of pineal hydroxy-indole-O-methyltransferase by psychotomimetic drugs." *J. Pharm. Pharmacol.,* 25 (1973), pp. 751-752.

[50] Heinze, W., et al.: "The acute and chronic effect of

5-methoxy-tryptamine on selected members of a primate social colony," *Biol. Psychiatry,* 15 (1980), pp. 829-838.

[51] Hess, S.M., Redfield, B.G., and Udenfriend, S.: "The effect of monoamine oxidase inhibitors and tryptophan on the tryptamine content of animal tissues and urine," *J. Pharmacol. Exp. Ther.,* 127 (1959), pp. 178-181.

[52] Himwich, H.E., Kety, S.S., and Smythies, J.R., (eds.): *Amines and Schizophrenia,* Pergamon Press, 1967.

[53] ———: "Introductory Remarks" to symposium, "Effects of Hallucinogenic Drugs in Man," *Federation Proc.,* Vol. 20, No. 4 (December 1961), pp. 874-875.

[54] Hofmann, A., et al.: *Experientia,* 14 (1958), p. 107.

[55] Holmstedt, B.: "Tryptamine derivatives in Epena, an intoxicating snuff used by some South American Indians," *Arch. Int. Pharmacodyn. Ther.,* 156 (1965), pp. 285-305.

[56] Horowitz, M. and C. Palmer: *Shaman Woman/Mainline Lady: Women's Writings on the Drug Experience.*

[57] Jacobs, B.L. (ed.): *Hallucinogens: Neurochemical, Behavioral and Clinical Perspectives,* Raven Press, New York, 1984.

[58] Janiger, Oscar: verbal communication, February 1991.

[59] Karkkainen, J., et al.: "Urinary excretion of free bufotenin by psychiatric patients," *Biol. Psychiatry,* 24 (1988), pp. 441-446.

[60] Kensinger, K.M.: *"Banisteriopsis* Usage Among the Peruvian Cashinahua," in Harner [48], pp. 9-14.

[61] Kety, S.S.: "Possible relation of central amines to behavior in schizophrenic patients," *Federation Proc.,* Vol. 20, No. 4 (December 1961), pp. 894-896.

[62] Kusel, H.: "Ayahuasca Drinkers among the Chama Indians of North-East Peru," *Psychedelic Review* 6 (1965), pp. 58-66.

[63] Leary, T.: "Programmed Communication during Experiences with DMT (Dimethyltryptamine)," *Psychedelic Review,* 8, (1966), pp. 83-95.

[64] Lipton, M.A., DiMascio, A., and Killam, K.F. (eds.): *Psychopharmacology: A Generation of Progress,* Raven Press, 1978.

[65] Mandel. L., and Walker, R.: "The biosynthesis of 5-methoxy-N,N-dimethyltryptamine in vitro," *Life Sci.,* 15 (1971), pp. 1457-1463.

[66] McKenna, D.: "Biochemistry and pharmacology of tryptamines and beta-carbolines: A minireview," *J. Psychoactive Drugs,* 16 (1984), pp. 347-357.

[67] ———— et al.: "Differential Interactions of Indolealkylamines with 5-Hydroxytryptamine Receptor Subtypes," *Neuropharmacology,* 29 (1990), pp. 193-198.

[68] ———— and McKenna, T.: *The Invisible Landscape,* Seabury Press, 1975.

[69] McKenna, T.: "Among Ayahuasquera," in Rätsch [84], pp. 179-211.

[70] ————: *Wahre Halluzinationen* (Gaia Media AG, 1991).

[71] ————: *True Hallucinations* (8 tapes, Lux Natura).

[72] ————: *Tryptamine Hallucinogens and Consciousness* (tape, Lux Natura).

[73] ————: *Psilocybin and the Sands of Time* (tape, Lux Natura).

[74] ————: and Abraham, R.: *New Maps of Hyperspace* (tape, Lux Natura).

[75] McLeod, W.R., and Sitaram, B.R.: "Bufotenine reconsidered," *Acta psychiatr. scan.,* 72 (1985), pp. 447-450.

[76] Metzner, R.: "The Pharmacology of Psychedelic Drugs," *Psychedelic Review,* 1 (1963), pp. 69-115.

[77] ————: "Hallucinogens in Contemporary North American Shamanic Practice," *Proceedings of the Fourth International Conference of the Study of Shamanism and Alternate Modes of Healing* (1987), p. 171-175.

[78] Misztal, S.: Synteza N,N-dwumetylo-5-hydroksytryptaminy I

N-Metylo-5-metoksytryptaminy," *Diss. Pharmaceut.*, 11 (1959), pp. 11-15.

[79] Murphree, H.B., et al.: "Effects in Normal Man of α-methyltryptamine and α-ethyltryptamine," *Clin. Pharmacol. Therapeut.*, 2 (1961), pp. 722-726.

[80] Naranjo C.: "Psychotherapeutic possibilities of new fantasy-enhancing drugs," *Clin. Toxicol.*, 2 (1969), pp. 209-224.

[81] Nichols, David E., and Glennon, Richard A.: "Medicinal Chemistry and Structure-Activity Relationships of Hallucinogens," in Jacobs [57], pp. 95-142.

[82] ————: "Studies of the relationship between molecular structure and hallucinogenic activity," *Pharmac. Biochem. Behav.*, 24 (1986), pp. 335-340.

[83] Pfeifer, A.K., Sátory, E., Pataky, I., and Vizy, E.: "Einfluss der Tranquillantien auf die Wirkung von Diäthyltryptamine (DET)," *Acta Physiol. Acad. Sci. Hung.* 18(1961), pp. 82-83.

[84] Rätsch, C. (ed.): *Gateway to Inner Space*, Prism Press, 1989.

[85] Repke, D.B., Grotjahn, D.B., and Shulgin, A.T.: "Psychotomimetic N-methyl-N-isopropyl-tryptamines. Effects of variation of aromatic oxygen substituents," *J. Med. Chem.*, 28, pp, 892-896.

[86] Richards, W.A., et al: "The peak experience variable in DPT-assisted psychotherapy with cancer patients," *J. Psychedelic Drugs*, 9 (1977), pp. 1-10.

[87] Richman, G.D. "The Santo Daime Doctrine: an interview with Alix Polari: de Alverga" *Shaman's Drum*, 22 (1990-91), pp. 30-41.

[88] Rivier, L. and Lindgren, J.E.: "Ayahuasca, the South American Halllucinogenic drink: an ethnobotanical and chemical investigation," *Econ. Bot.* 26 (1972), pp. 101-129.

[89] Rosenberg, D.E., Isbell, H., and Miner, E.J.: "Comparison of a placebo, N-dimethyltryptamine and 6-hydroxy-N-di-

methyltryptamine in man," *Psychopharmocologia,* 4 (1963), pp. 39-42.

[90] Saavedra, J., and Axelrod, J.: "Psychotomimetic N-methylated tryptamines: Formation in brain in vivo and in vitro," *Science,* 175, pp. 1365-1366.

[91] Sai-Halasz, A., Brunecker, G., and Szara, S.: *Psych. Neurol.,* 135 (1958), p. 285.

[92] ―――― and Endroczy, E.: "The Effect of Tryptamine Derivatives on the Behaviour of Dogs During Brain-Stem Stimulation," in [10], pp. 405-407.

[93] Sátory, E., Pfeifer, A.K., Pataky, I., and Kerekes, L.: "Die Wirkung von Diäthyltryptamin auf die Monoaminoxydase-Aktivität," *Acta Physiol. Acad. Sci. Hung.,* 18 (1961), p. 83.

[94] Schlemmer, R.F., et al.: "The effect of a hallucinogen, 5-methoxy-N,N-dimethyltryptamine, on primate social behavior," *Commun. Psychoparmacol.,* 1 (1977), pp. 105-118.

[95] Schultes. R.E.: "Botanical Sources of the New World Narcotics," *Psychedelic Review,* 2 (1963), pp. 145-166. Reprinted in Weil [129].

[96] ――――: *Where the Gods Reign,* Synergetic Press, 1988.

[97] ――――: and Hofmann, A.: *Plants of the Gods: Origins of Hallucinogenic Use,* McGraw-Hill, 1979.

[98] ――――and――――: *The Botany and Chemistry of Hallucinogens,* revised and enlarged second edition, Thomas, 1988.

[99] Shulgin, A.T., and Carter, M.F.: "N,N-Diisopropyltryptamine (DIPT) and 5-methoxy-N,N-diisopropyltryptamine (5-MeO-DIPT). Two orally active tryptamine analogs with CNS activity," *Psychopharmacol. Commun.,* 1 (1975), pp. 93-98.

[100] Siegel, R.K., and Jarvik, M.E.: "DMT self-administration by monkeys in isolation," *Bull. Psychonomic Soc.,* 16 (1980), pp. 117-120.

[101] ――――: *Intoxication,* Simon & Schuster, 1989.

[102] Smith, M.V.: *Psychedelic Chemistry.*

[103] Smythies, J.R., Bradley, R.J., and Johnson, V.S.: "The behavioral effects of some derivatives of mescaline and N,N-dimethyltryptamine in the rat," *Life Sci.*, 6 (1967), pp. 1887-1893.

[104] ———, Morin, R.D., and Brown, G.D.: "Identification of dimethyltryptamine and O-methylbufotenine in human cerebrospinal fluid by combined gas chromatography/mass spectrometry," *Biol. Psychiat.*, 14 (1979), pp. 549-556.

[105] Solomon, P. (ed.): *Psychiatric Drugs,* Grune & Stratton, 1966.

[106] Soskin, R.A.: "Dipropyltryptamine in psychotherapy," *Curr. Psychiatr. Ther.*, 15 (1975), pp. 147-156.

[107] ———, Grof, S., and Richards, W.A.: "Low doses of dipropyltryptamine in psychotherapy," *Arch. Gen. Psychiatry,* 28 (1973), pp. 817-822.

[108] Stafford, P.: *Psychedelics Encyclopedia,* revised edition, J.P. Tarcher, 1983.

[109] Stillman, R.C., and Willette, R.E. (eds.): *The Psychopharmacology of Hallucinogens,* Pergamon, 1978.

[110] Strassman, R.: "The Pineal Gland: Current Evidence for its Role in Consciousness," *Psychedelic Monographs and Essays,* 5 (1991), pp. 167-205.

[111] ———: correspondence, 1990-91.

[112] Szára, S.: "Dimethyltryptamine: Its metabolism in man; the relation of its psychotic effect to serotonin metabolism," *Experientia*, 12, p. 441.

[113] ———: "The comparison of the psychotic effect of tryptamine derivatives with the effects of mescaline and LSD-25 in self experiments," in [30], pp. 460-467.

[114] ———: "Hallucinogenic effects and metabolism of tryptamine derivatives in man," *Federation Proc.*, 20 (1961), pp. 885-888.

[115] ———: "Correlation between metabolism and behavioral action of psychotropic tryptamine derivatives," *Biochem. Pharmacol.*, 8 (1961), p. 32.

[116] ————: "Effect of psychotropic tryptamine derivatives on the regional distribution of serotonin in the brain," in Bradley [10].

[117] ————: "Behavioral correlates of 6-hydroxylation and the effect of psychotropic tryptamine derivatives on brain serotonin levels," in Richter [87], pp. 432-452.

[118] ————, and Axelrod, J.: "Hydroxylation and N-demethylation of N,N-dimethyltryptamine," *Experientia,* 15 (1959), pp. 216-219.

[119] ————, ————, and Hearst, E.: "The 6-hydroxylation of tryptamine derivatives: a way of producing psychoactive metabolites," *Ann. N.Y. Acad. Sci.,* 96 (1962), pp. 134-141.

[120] ————, ————, and ————: "Metabolism of Hallucinogenic Tryptamine Derivatives" (intro. by J. Axelrod), Clinical Neuropharmacology Research Center, NIMH. Abstract in *Federation Proc.*, 19 (1960), p. 23.

[121] ————, ————, and ————: "Metabolism and behavioral action of psychotropic tryptamine homologues," *Int. J. Neuropharmacol.,* 1 (1962), pp. 111-117.

[122] ————, Hearst, E., and Putney, F.: "Metabolism and behavioral action of psychotropic tryptamine homologues," *Int. J. Neuropharmacol.,* 1 (1962), pp. 111-117.

[123] ————, et al.: "Psychological effects and metabolism of N,N-diethyltryptamine in man," *Arch. Gen. Psychiatry,* 15 (1966), pp. 320-329.

[124] Taborsky, R.G., Delvigs, P., and Page, I.H.: "6-Hydroxylation: Effect on the psychotropic potency of tryptamines," *Science,* 153 (1966), pp. 1018-1020.

[125] Tanimukai, H., et al.: "Detection of psychotomimetic N,N-dimethylated indoleamines in the urine of four schizophrenic patients," *Brit. J. Psychiat.,* 117 (1970), pp. 421-430.

[126] Turner, W.J., and Merlis, S.: "Effect of Some Indolealkylamines on Man," A.M.A. *Archives of Neurology and Psychiatry,* 81 (January 1959), p. 121.

[127] Uyeno, E.T.: "6-Hydroxylated N,N-dimethyltryptamines and hallucinogenic potency," *Proc. West. Pharmacol. Soc.,* 12 (1969), pp. 118-123.

[128] Weidmann, H., and Cerletti, A.: "Studies on psilocybin and related compounds," *Helv Physiol. Acta,* 18 (1960), pp. 174-182.

[129] Weil, G.M., Metzner, R., and Leary, T. (eds.): *The Psychedelic Reader* (selected articles from *Psychedelic Review*) University Books, 1965.

[130] Wieland, T., and Motsel, W.: "Über das Vorkommen von bufotenin im gelben Knollenblätterpilz," *Liebig. Ann. Chem.,* 581 (1953), pp. 10-16.

[131] Wyatt, R., Saavedra, J., and Axelrod, J.: "A dimethyltryptamine-forming enzyme in human blood," *Am. J. Psychiatry,* 130 (1973), pp. 754-760.

EMBRYONIC HOLOGRAPHY

by Richard Alan Miller and Burt Webb

Introduction

Holography is the process of recording and recreating complex three-dimensional wave fronts in space. The holography with which we are most familiar deals mostly with the visible spectrum, so we tend to think of holography in terms of three-dimensional photography.

However, holography can be conceived in different realms of the spectrum. The whole process of lasers and laser abilities to create images in space in visible light radiation is closely connected to microwave research and a device called a "maser" which broadcasts coherent radiation of microwave frequencies. It should be possible in theory, with the proper kind of equipment, to capture and broadcast complex three-dimensional wave form structures in space across a whole broad band of the electromagnetic spectrum. We can call this "broad band holography." Henceforth in this paper, when we are dealing with the term "holography" we suggest that it means a whole range of processes for capturing wave forms at different frequencies on the spectrum.

Some of the interesting properties of holography have to do with its differences from photography. In photography, the light from an object is reflected onto a flat surface where it essentially discolors that surface; or rather, the shadow that it casts discolors that surface. If you cut a photograph in half, you have half of the original picture that you started with. Holography is quite different.

In a hologram, the pattern of light that is created by the object is recorded at each point of the film. Each contains the whole image. Each image is slightly different, however, and all of the images are very vague and very fuzzy.

Detail in a photograph is not particularly connected to the size in the sense that a small piece of a photograph will have a lot of detail on a small area of the scene. A large photograph will have a lot of detail on all of the scene. In a hologram, each grain has some of the information about the whole scene. It has some detail about the *whole* scene. A large hologram has a lot of details about the whole scene. So something different happens when you cut a hologram in half: you get the original picture, but it is less clear because you have lost detail.

A lot of work has been done recently (for over 30 years) on the electromagnetic field phenomena that are associated with the biological processes. The idea is nothing new, of course. Farraday did some experimentation with animal electricity, and Galvanni (with his Galvanic cells) did experiments with animals. It was quite understandable in the growth of science to accept life as being electronic.

However, within the last 50 years, our intense activity in the biological field and the breakthrough in molecular biology (DNA research, etc.) have tended to obscure some deeper questions as to our understanding the nature of life. We are reaching the end of the paradigm in which we can afford to ignore the electronic properties of the macrosystem and deal with chemistry as if it were taking place in a neutral system. This new field can be termed "bioelectronic": a term based on biophysics.

Conventional biophysics seems to be centered around very minute detail of things, such as ion exchanges across cell membranes, etc. And very, very little contact is made with the idea that the electromagnetic systems may regulate the whole organism, the whole multicellular system, and not merely function at the level of cells. The regulation of the nervous system is appreciated to be primarily a biochemical phenomena in the sense that it is the exchange or profusion of calcium and potassium across a cell membrane. And so what you essentially have is a ripple effect that travels down the process of the cell, caused by an exchange of ions. Thus it is a chemical signal. And the synapse transmits, again, chemical, so that you have another chemical signal, and even though electromagnetics is appreciated in the nervous system, it is seen as an epi-phenomena. In other words, not really appreciated as being integral or central to the regulation of the system. However, the theories of regulation of the system are very poor. And they do no justice to the complexity and subtlety of a living process.

Some of the specific electronic characteristics in the cell could pertain to the presence or absence of various chemicals that either accept or donate electrons. Electron donation or electron acceptance are connected to the older ideas of acids and bases, of chemical processes called oxidation and reduction. One must then approach a biological solution, or interior body fluids, on the basis of the electrolytes in solution: The different ionized and charged particles. Both kinds exist. And this is only the beginning.

We must deal with the fields that exist, the potentials and

the polarities. And between the two of them the charged particles in the fields would then begin to generate the flows. Then we must deal with a process called electrophoresis, which is the movement of small particles by an electrostatic field. And we could also see the possibility of electrodynamic fields moving the particles in waves. What we have, essentially, is a solution of charged particles under a very complex control via a complicated electromagnetic field system that moves those solutions around. But in moving the solutions, the charged distributions inside the organism change and modify the fields. There is a very complex feedback between flows of particles and electromagnetic fields.

We have an incredibly complex situation compared to a motor in which a simple electromagnetic field system is cut by a simple metallic conductor. We have an organic system in which a simple electromagnetic field system is cut by a simple metallic conductor. We have an organic system in which there are literally millions—billions—enormous numbers of fields being generated by enormous numbers of particles, being created, changed, switched around, etc. So we have a possible interaction between the structure of a physical system and the fluid flows within that system, with the heart being one of the most profound of those fluid flows. The heart could be seen as setting up a basic system of waves of movement that form the basis—the fundamental note—of the organic system.

There are many other interesting bioelectronic characteristics. One of the most fascinating is the fact that protein-formed structures in the cellular space are based upon the charged distribution across their surface; the charged distribution is related to the sequence of amino acids in their particular side-chains and determines tendencies to act. Amino acids have been characterized as being semiconductor in nature on the basis of one end being an electron acceptor and the other one being a electron donor. These link up into chains. And then they have little side-spines, and these side-spines also have their characteristics.

It is possible that charge movement takes place across the surface of a protein. A line of side-chains stick out of the surface of protein molecules, forming a charge distribution system that acts almost like an electrical conductor. The electrons could hop along the spines sticking out from the side of the protein molecule and actually flow across the surface as if they were going in a conductor. We have the possibility of electron conduction across the surface of the protein.

We have any number of interesting prostheses, or special radicals in the sense of molecular substructures, that have a whole host of purposes. For instance, the hem- of hemoglobin in a very fascinating iron prosthesis. There is a figure of iron and other items arrayed in space; very small compared to the size of the globin molecule to which it is attached, but very effective for acting as a grappling hook for oxygen.

This is also under electronic control. We have the possibility of the rotation of the different parts of the molecule, if it breaks into several different sections in the sense that they are cohesive units, and those units are chained together. If those units change through a flow of electrons or through an input of a charge from the chemical space, then the shape could change. So charge flow and charge distribution on a protein molecule is critical to change in the shape.

There is evidence of special tissue in the back of rats, in fatty pads, that can uncouple the oxidation energy instead of converting to ATP as is the usual process at the level of ribosomes. The special enzymes convert the oxidation energy directly into infrared radiation and radiate it out of their bodies. So it is conceivable that radiation of infrared takes place as a result of bioelectronic processes on protein.

Another possibility is that of visible light in the various

creatures that are able to glow. This process is carried on by special enzymes. And again, we have the different processes that are electronically keyed and involve electronic radiation.

Microwaves have been detected in the regions of the brain and the heart of men and rabbits as indicated in recent research projects. We see that a living organic system is a very complex holographic entity. And by holographic it is meant that we have seen different things that are done at the molecular level through complex EM activity and then we have conceived of flows and fields at the organismic level. Let us speak of the creation of those fields, or rather, the coordination of those fields.

In the nuclei of each cell in the human body, the DNA (dioxyribo-nucleic acid) carries the structure of our whole body. Not just our physical form, but also the processes that that form undergoes in terms of survival. If all of these things are in truth locked in the DNA, how does that turn into a functioning being?

The DNA could possibly be the holographic projectors. The DNA could be projecting a field that would be experienced by other DNA in the body. The DNA, in a sense, could be linked together. The DNA are also linked to their own cells that they are controlling via mechanisms of RNA transfer and enzymatic action in the cell. We believe that it is likely that the DNA and the RNA are in communication. Recent research has shown the possibility that DNA activates the motion of an RNA sphincter or iris mechanism to permit or exclude ion entrance into the cell. If this is, in fact, true, —and if the DNA controls the action of the RNA that goes to the ribosomes and other sites to create specific enzymes in the cell which causes further reaction, it is possible that the enzymes are under the control of the DNA also.

We believe that the DNA is the projector of the biohologram, both at the cellular level and at the whole-organismic level.

This means that the DNA creates a situation of a complex pattern of three-dimensional electromagnetic standing and moving wave fronts in the space that the organism occupies. We believe that these wave fronts interact with, interpenetrate with, and inter-determine the physical substance that makes up the creature.

The biohologram has characteristic properties of affecting the DNA that occupies its specific position within the biohologram. We believe that the nervous system constitutes a coordination mechanism that integrates DNA projections of the rest of the cells in the system. We believe it is first and foremost a coordination mechanism. And it aligns these cellular holograms and the linkage of the whole creature hologram. The DNA in a particular cell is not totally active. It has been determined that there may be as little as 1% of the DNA present in the nucleus of the cell acting as the determinant for the structure of that cell. The nervous system, interestingly enough, has the highest percentage of operating DNA of any cell system in the body, of up to at least 10% of the DNA in the brain cells. The neuron nuclei are most active.

We suggest that the nervous system projects a biohologram which interacts with the cellular bioholograms. If the membrane structure of the neuron nuclei are examined closely, it will be seen that the different cavity systems that enter the outer membrane, and also enter the inner membranes, will be seen to topologically be a single membrane. So the nucleus is lacking a membrane, or the neurons are lacking a membrane in the sense that two of their membranes are topologically one membrane.

We suggest that the neurons are not actually brain cells as such. We believe that the brain is the cell, and the neurons are like a distributed nucleus for that cell. That makes the glial cells organelles in the giant brain-cell. But they are also cells in their own right, much more so than neurons are. We believe the glials are infinitely involved with the biohologram, in its projections and its coordination.

To go further, the biohologram, projected by the brain, creates standing and moving electromagnetic wave patterns at different frequencies of the spectrum in order to effect different biochemical transformations. There may be specific electro-static fields, or there may be electrodynamic fields varying at various frequencies all the way up the spectrum into visible light and beyond, from low radio waves.

Another process of holography is called "acoustical holography." Acoustical holography employs sound waves to create a movement on a surface that is used as the basis for creation of an optical hologram. So we essentially convert between a pattern of sound waves reflected off an object in space into a pattern of light waves that can reconstruct the shape of that object. We have a transformation between two levels of vibration, two media as it were, preserving a pattern in space. We suggest that this happens to a much greater degree in the DNA control of our bodies. The liver, for example, contains special function cells. The special function of the liver cells is created by the influence of the projection of the liver pattern on the DNA in the cells in the area where the liver is created. We are suggesting an important feedback mechanism between the activation of the DNA in a particular cellular tissue type that causes it to be that tissue type, and the biohologram being projected by the nervous system. This is bioholography.

Conception

Human sexuality is usually viewed as a physical-chemical complex; a more coherent viewpoint would see human sexuality in terms of electronics. We will not go into the detail of the electronic behavior of the nervous system of the human being during intercourse. But we will begin the story with ovulation.

Researchers have found that at the moment of ovulation there is a definite shift in the electrical fields of the body of the woman. The membrane in the follicle bursts and the egg passes down the fallopian tubes. As a side note, we feel that the phases of the moon quite probably influence the permeability of the membrane in the follicle, making it more likely that the egg will pass down the fallopian tubes at certain periods of time. The sperm is negative with respect to the egg. When the sperm and the egg unite, the membrane around the egg becomes hyperpolarized. It is at this moment that the electromagnetic entity is formed.

The fertilized egg cell contains all information necessary to create a complete operational human being. And furthermore, the biohologram begins to function at conception, and only ceases to function at death.

So perhaps conception is the proper place to mark the beginning of the individual.

The zygote begins to divide as it travels down the fallopian tube. It is quite possible that it navigates its passage partially by sensing the biohologram of the mother. And this may actually assist in approaching and attaching to the wall of the uterus.

As soon as attachment to the wall of the uterus is complete, the zygote begins the process of establishing the linkage with the mother's circulatory system that will permit the passage of blood carrying important nutrients into the zygote. The womb is a special electronic environment in which an electrolytic solution provides an excellent framework for electromagnetic effects which are necessary in the development of the egg.

Development

The developing zygote is spherical in shape at first. Then it flattens to become the embryonic disk. The disk differentiates into three layers: the inner layer (the endoderm) will become the viscera—digestion, blood, etc.; the middle layer (the mysoderm) will become the musculature; and the outer layer (the ectoderm), furthest away from the wall of the uterus, will become the nervous system and the skin.

Very early in development, one of the first appearances of discrete structure has to do with the formation of the neural tube. From a point in the center of the embryonic disk, a line defines itself out to the edge of the disk—a radial line. On both sides of this line, which is called the neural groove, the flesh puckers up and curves over to form a tube. This is called the neural tube. Both ends of the neural tube are open, originally. And we feel that it is possible field lines could pass through the tube. The tube is actually entrapping electro-magnetic lines of force. Eventually the tube closes on both ends, trapping the amniotic flue in the cerebrospinal space. We are suggesting that cerebrospinal fluid is an analog of amniotic fluid that the embryo develops in. We think that the nervous system, and most especially the brain, retains some embryonic properties all during the life of the organism in question. It is a safe assumption that the brain is, in a sense, the most infantile tissue in the body. As we mentioned before, the greatest part of the genome is active in the brain, and this agrees well with the idea that it is neoembryonic in a sense because originally all of the genome or the DNA in the nucleus of the embryonic cells is functional. It is only with development that most of the genome shuts down and specific cells begin to function, operating on only a fraction of their DNA potential.

With the formation of the neural tube, one end (the end that is in the center of the embryonic disk) begins to expand and enfold, twist, and develop itself into a system of complex tissues in complicated geometrical structures, which will become the structure of the brain of the creature. It is our contention that the brain is necessary and the nervous system is necessary for the development of the creature. It is one of the earliest formations and is prior to the generation of most of the structure of the body. Our contention is that the DNA at the center of each cell creates the multicellular creature hologram by influencing the DNA in the center of the cells. Initially, the problem of development centers around the flow of materials through space, and the establishment of material structure at discrete locations in space.

The study of cymatics has to do with the creation of structures due to the resonance of wave patterns. As an example, in two dimensions, if a drumhead is covered with fine sand and then is caused to vibrate by drawing a violin bow across the edge of the diaphragm or drumhead, the sand will arrange itself in geometrical patterns. It will flow into lines that mark nodal lines of zero motion that separate zones of the drumhead that are moving in different directions. The simplest would be a single line that would be a diameter of the drumhead, signifying that one half was pulsating differently than the other half. But the line between them is not moving. This is very important to an understanding of biological development.

We believe that the biohologram projected by the embryonic nervous system forms a three-dimensional pattern of resonant structures; including points, lines, and planes that electro-magnetically behave as the acoustic waves—the material waves—of the drumhead. In other words, these electromagnetic points, lines and planes form locations of no movement. Essentially the matter that is flowing, the electrolytic solutions that are flowing, that have been drawn from the blood of the mother, are caused to move rhythmically through the developing embryo. As they reach certain points, lines and planes, their motion stops. This is where structures are laid down and built up. This process is the key to embryonic holography.

The zygote acts like a three-dimensional nozzle. Electrolytes from the bloodstream of the mother flow through this nozzle and into the cymatic structure of standing wave patterns distributed through space inside the embryo and become fixed, solidified structures. This accounts for the different zones and the separation of the zones of the different kinds of tissue groups.

The picture is completed by the effects of the biohologram on the DNA of the cells that have formed along with the migration of the substances. You have an actual migration of cells, and a migration of substances throughout the embryo that take up locations dependent upon resonant structures of standing wave patterns. The cells, having arrived at their proper location and beginning to involve themselves with the materials and the fluids that are flowing in the three-dimensional nozzle are then specified in their particular tissue nature by the biohologram being projected by the nervous system. They are refined and developed as their genome is shut down until only the DNA that operates in a particular cell is just that DNA which defines the structure and operation of that particular kind of tissue group. So, through a complex interaction of three-dimensional electromagnetic fields, rapidly dividing cells and a flow of electrolytes that is directed by the field but also feeds back on the field and influences it, a multicellular creature achieves the proper structure that will permit it to exist apart from the specialized environment of the womb.

This brings us to the close of the embryological development. When the proper point is reached at which a potentially self-sustaining entity has been created, then the conditions begin to change, leading to the expulsion of the new self-sufficient entity from the womb of the mother. We are now ready to enter another section that concerns itself with the postnatal stabilization of the new entity.

Postnatal Development

Birth occurs. The fetus is expelled from the electromagnetic environment of the womb, and enters a world of separate gases, liquids, and solids. The biohologram which lead to the development and stabilization of the entity now takes on its important control behavior that is necessary to keep the organism alive and well throughout its whole life. The biohologram changes its action with the change in media. Its responsibility is no longer the actual development of structures, but rather the regulation of processes within those structures. Very little has been said about the potential interaction of the biohologram of the mother and the developing baby. We do not know very much, except that the possibility exists. However, at the moment of birth that intimate interlocking of holograms ceases to exist.

Now the entity enters the world in which it is alone, in a sense that only under certain conditions can it interact bioholographically with other creatures. Evidence has been found that certain kinds of salamanders have a complex system of electromagnetic sensing that is based on a string of spots along the side of the salamander. As long as this salamander is in salt water, which is an excellent electromagnetic conductor, this system of spots serves to detect three-dimensional electromagnetic field changes around the salamander, thereby alerting it to food, enemies, etc. But the salamander spends part of its time on dry land. When it comes out on dry land, its holographic detection system withers away and ceases to function because there is not a medium that will sustain the electromagnetic fields necessary. However, when the salamander reenters the water, the holographic detection system comes back into operation. We suggest that humans and other multicellular land creatures have such an external holographic detection system in the womb. But that just like the salamander that external system tends to atrophy in the atmosphere because it does not have sufficient media to sustain the necessary electromagnetic fields. However, there is still a very slight leakage of the biohologram beyond the skin of the entity.

We feel that this slight leakage is the basis of a great deal of paranormal phenomena and is definitely the origin of the concept of the aura.

Under certain circumstances and in certain individuals in abnormal states, the projected biofield becomes faintly visible. It is possible, as recent research has shown, that the human eye can detect other frequencies than the strictly visual frequencies of light, that the leaking biohologram may actually be on a different frequency than the visible spectrum. And our eyes are merely transducing it, or translating it, into the visible spectrum. So we feel that the aura is intimately connected to the biohologram that causes the body to continue to function properly. We will return later to some other interesting facets of the manipulation of the biohologram. For the moment, we will simply say that dowsing might possibly be related to an external functioning of the bioholographic system of the organism. Experiments have shown that dowsers detect extremely minute changes in geomagnetism. And these minute changes are most probably connected to the presence of water underground. We are mostly water, and the structuring of water in our systems is very closely connected to the bioelectronic behavior of our systems. So it is conceivable that we have some sort of sympathetic resonance that can permit us to detect a very tiny minute magnetic field change that is associated with underground water.

Ionization of the air is extremely important to our health. Ionization of the air also would potentially permit the expansion of the bioholograms further beyond the skin, or the expansion of what is commonly called the aura. We find that areas of high ionization (such as mountaintops, seacoasts, areas around waterfalls, etc.) have been known since time immemorial as holy or magical places. This might be connected to the fact that the increased ionization in the atmosphere permits the expansion of the aura or biohologram to the extent that bioholograms of individuals can interact or to the extent than an individual can manipulate this biohologram to cause external effects that would be perceived by the ancient superstitious people as magic.

As long as the biohologram is functioning properly, as long as the nervous system is continuing to coordinate and project the complex three-dimensional fields that support the biological processes in the organism, the organism survives. When the biohologram ceases to function properly, the organism suffers. And when the principle action of the biohologram stops, the organism dies. If there is any scientific correlate to the concept of Soul, it is most probably this bioholographic pattern system. It is composed of the ultimate stuff of the universe, electromagnetic field energy, which does not die in the sense that creatures die, so it fulfills the attribute of the Soul of being immortal in that sense. However, the pattern does change with growth, with learning, with experience, and with age. So there is a development of the Soul or the electronic field entity. It is conceivable, although a great deal more research needs to be done, that the electromagnetic field entity might be capable of an independent existence which would form the basis for the concept of life after death. However, a free electromagnetic field entity without a biophysiological matrix might have a difficult time in interacting with creatures, such as ourselves, that are still utilizing the biophysiological matrix.

This might be the origin of stories of ghosts and so forth, in which a disembodied biohologram attempting to communicate with a physical creature could only enter the nervous system of the creature and cause hallucinations of forms in space that upon examination disappear, or turn out to be merely hallucinations, having no scientifically verifiable existence.

Regeneration

In reptiles, tissue regeneration of a profound nature is possible. Entire limbs can be replaced. The process goes something like this:

A leg is lost. The damaged cells on the stump revert back to a neoembryonic condition. They now undergo explosive growth. The growth slows as the crude size and shape of the leg reappears. Refinement continues. Details appear. Growth slows even further. And finally, a new leg exists.

Such regeneration is not possible in mammals. Several reasons suggest themselves, but we favor the concept that the greater detail and sophistication of the biological machinery in mammals is made possible by the greater sophistication of the bioholographic projection system, which we call the nervous system. It is the recreation of the nerve linkages that permit the very sophisticated fields to exist, that define our appendages, that is lacking. We can generate new tissue, but to regenerate nerve cells seems to be much more difficult. And without those nerve cells being present in the new limb, the final sophisticated states of coordination are not possible.

Many theorists are now tending toward the concept that cancerous tissue is tissue that has been damaged in some fashion and has reverted to a neoembryonic condition. However, because the necessary coordination control is not possible for regeneration to proceed, the cancerous tissue is stuck in the earliest stages of regeneration and merely continues to divide and expand without any control whatsoever. We also believe that this behavior is electromagnetic in the sense that the cancerous tissue has changed its electromagnetic properties to such a great degree that the physical biohologram is no longer capable of controlling the tissue. Therefore, it is in a runaway condition.

If this is actually true, that cancerous tissue is runaway neo-embryonic tissue caused by a partially functioning regeneration system, then if we can understand the process better, not only could we control cancer, but even more important and profound, we may be able to unlock the key of complex mammalian regeneration processes. So that some day it may be possible to regenerate an entire limb that has been lost from a mammal, up to and including human beings.

Becker, in a series of experiments, has shown that bone regeneration can be tripled in speed by the proper application of electromagnetic fields from the outside with no implants necessary. This proves that EM fields have a profound role in the generation and coordination of biological structures.

As mentioned earlier, we feel that the biohologram is closely connected by paranormal phenomena. It is quite possible that psychic healers who "lay on hands" are, in essence, exporting the power of their own bioholograms and asserting the control of that biohologram over the sick, weak biohologram that has permitted the disease condition to occur in the patient. Just in the way that two oscillators that are connected will tend toward the frequency of the more powerful oscillator, if two biohologram systems are connected, the more powerful biohologram may entrain the weaker biohologram and restore it to its proper coordination function.

It is possible that psychic surgery occurs via a process of the location of the diseased tissue through EM sensing inasmuch as diseased tissue has different electromagnetic properties than healthy tissue. An invasion of the body of the patient by the hand of the psychic surgeon occurs through manipulation of electro-magnetic fields that actually cause the skin to part and help to locate the diseased tissue and then cause the skin to reclose. It has been shown in experiments that blood will not clot if the polarity on the outside of the blood vessel is reversed from its natural, undamaged condition. In other words, when a blood vessel is damaged, its polarity changes. If we can prevent that polarity change, we can prevent blood from clotting. This may even explain the mastery of bloodless, tool-less psychic surgery in which a surgeon with his bare hands can enter a human body and withdraw without leaving a cut. It is more an actual interaction between bioholograms than an actual interaction between physical substances. The physical substances are moved aside and the rejoined by the operation of the biohologram, thereby preventing the loss of blood or the appearance of a scar.

In closing, we should like to state that the earth, the sun, and the galaxy are all very complex electromagnetic entities; and that we feel that from the earliest existence of a bioholographic entity in the womb, the sun, earth, moon, other planets, and even stars beyond the solar system influence and to some extent direct the development of the entity.

This is a very concrete electro-magnetic connection that could serve as a scientific basis for explaining astrology.

Not only do these conditions influence prenatal development, but they are also present postnatally and continue to influence the organism in a variety of interesting ways. Evidence has come to light that the brain can intercept various frequencies of radiation from astronomical and terrestrial phenomena. If this is so, then it provides a very real scientific basis for the statement of the mystics that we are all inextricably woven into the fabric of the universe; we are not separate, distinct physical entities, but we are rather partial interacting electromagnetic entities that partake of the rich electromagnetic life of the universe. We will cover these concepts and the other concepts of paranormal-normal phenomena at a later date in other papers.

Holographic modeling is the next great revolution that awaits biology.

References

Ambrose, E.J., Osborne, J.S., and Stuart, P.R. "Structure and properties of the cell surface complex." In *Liquid Crystals and Ordered Fluids* (Johnson J.F., and Porter, R., eds.) New York: Plenum, 1970.

Becker, R.O., "The effect of magnetic fields upon the central nervous system." *Medical Electronics and Biological Engineering.* 1963. 1, 293-303.

Becker. R.O., "Electromagnetic forces and life process." *Technology Review.* December 1972.

Bernal, J.O. General discussion. *Transactions of the Faraday Society.* 193, 29, 1082.

Blair, Lawrence. *Rhythms of Vision.* New York: Warner Books, 1975.

Brown, F.A., Jr. "Electrical and magnetic sensitivity: Some orientational influences of nonvisual, terrestrial electromagnetic fields." *Annals, New York Academy of Science.* 1971. 188, 224-241.

Bulkley, D.H. "An electromagnetic model for dynamic turnover and the continuous self-replication of biological macromolecules." Rogue Press, 1973.

Burr, H.S. *Blueprint for Immortality.* London: Neville Spearman, 1972.

Burr, H.S., and Northrop, F.S.C. "The electrodynamic theory of life." *Quarterly Review of Biology.* 1935. 10, 322-333.

Elliot, H.C. "Neural tube and spinal cord." *Textbook of Neuro-anatomy.* Philadelphia: J.B. Lippincott Co., 1963.

Fowler, R.H., and Bernal, J.D. "Note on the pseudocrystalline structure of water." *Transactions of the Faraday Society.* 1933. 29, 1049.

Freedericksz, V. and Zolina, V. "Forces causing the orientation of an anisotropic liquid." *Transactions of the Faraday Society.* 193. 29, 919-944.

French, Vernon, Bryont, P.J., and Bryant, S.V. "Pattern regulation in epimorphic fields." *Science.* September 10, 1976. 969-981.

Garrison, W. "Destiny and geomagnetism." *Popular Electronics.* July 1971.

Koestler, A. *The Roots of Coincidence.* New York: Random House, 1972.

LeShan, L.A. "Toward a general theory of the paranormal." *Parapsychological Monographs.* 1969. No. 9.

Lund, E.J. *Bioelectric Fields and Growth.* Austin: University of Texas Press, 1945.

McGinnes, J.E. "Mobility gaps: A mechanism for band gaps in melanins." *Science.* 1972. 177, 896-897.

McKenna, T.J., and McKenna, D.J. "Organismic thought." *The Invisible Landscape.* New York: Seabury Press, 1975.

Miller, R.A., Webb, B., and Dickson, D. "Holographic concept of reality." *Psychoenergetic Systems.* 1975. Vol. 1, 55-62.

Muses. C.A. "On the modification of random fluctuations by a target-seeking process utilizing random energies." *Biomedical Computing.* 1970. 1, 75-80.

Needham, J. "The hierarchial continuity of biological order." *Order and Life.* 1936. 1, 109-168.

Presman, A.S. *Electromagnetic Fields and Life.* New York: Plenum, 1970.

Pullman, B., and Pullman, A. *Quantum Biochemistry.* New York: Interscience.

Purett, L. "Magnetic reversals and biological extinctions." *Science News.* 1971. 100, 287-302.

Ravitz, L.J. "Electromagnetic field monitoring of changing state-function, including hypnotic states." *Journal of the American Society of Psychosomatic Dentistry and Medicine.* 1970. 17, 119-129.

Szent-Gyorgyi, A. *Bioenergetics.* New York: Academic Press, 1957.

Szent-Gyorgyi, A. *Introduction to a Submolecular Biology.* New York: Academic Press, 1960.

Szent-Gyorgyi, A. *Electronic Biology and Cancer.* New York: Marcel Dekker, Inc., 1976.

Thom, R. *Structural Stability and Morphogenesis.* Massachusetts: W.A. Benjamin Press, 1975.

Tien, H.C. "Pattern recognition and psychosynthesis." *American Journal of Psychotherapy.* 1969. 23, 53-66.

Van Iterson, G., Jr. "A simple arrangement to demonstrate liquid crystals." *Transactions of the Faraday Society.* 1933. 29, 915-919.

Wheeler, J.A. "Geometrodynamics." Lectures; Course on Weak Interactions. Enrico Fermi Internal School of Physics. Varenna, Italy; Summer 1959.

BIBLIOTHECA PSYCHEDELICA

by Dr. Michael Montagne

—to Elvin Smith & his works
in memorium, February 1993

After years of struggle with regulatory authorities and public misconceptions, scientists, health professionals, and independent drug researchers are beginning to return to the study of psychedelic substances. Revitalization of psychedelic drug research for medical and spiritual applications is occurring around the world.

New clinical trials of various psychedelic drugs are being initiated in a number of countries. A group of Swiss psychiatrists formed the Swiss Medical Society for Psycholytic Therapy in 1985, and they have been granted permission by their government to use psychedelics in psychotherapy. The U.S. Food and Drug Administration's Drug Abuse Advisory Committee recommended, in July 1992, that medical research on psychedelics be expanded and new therapeutic applications be considered, following recent approval of protocols for new clinical testing. These are very positive signs of new and exciting inquiries into a class of drugs that almost were forgotten.

Rationale

With this renewed interest comes the need for intelligible, practical, and relevant information regarding the history, sources, uses, and functions of psychedelic drugs. The highest quality information begins with the "classic" literature, created through the activities and experiences of many individuals and groups. In this age of information, such knowledge provides a powerful basis for improving decision-making and enhancing the experiences and results of psychedelic drug use.

The cornerstone of both personal and societal knowledge about these drugs is the psychedelic library. Our understanding of the advantages and disadvantages of using these substances comes primarily from the classic literature, especially the working texts, on psychedelic drugs, their effects and applications, and problems resulting from their use. Additional literature covering more specific, detailed aspects of psychedelic drugs should supplement the working texts. One approach for identifying this literature and building a personal library is described herein.[1]

The literature on psychedelic drugs can appear confusing, because for over two centuries these substances have been defined and categorized in many different ways. In particular, a great variety of words and phrases have been proposed to describe the highly variable and remarkable effects of psychedelic drugs. Early reports of visionary drug experiences (in the 19th century) focused mostly on opium and cannabis. Plant substances now thought of as hallucinogens have been studied by Westerners mostly in the 20th century. Indigenous societies around the world have much longer, traditional relationships with native plant substances. Classifying drugs by their effects can be problematic, especially those substances producing hallucinatory, visionary, mystical, or creative states, and impossible when it comes to the ineffable aspects of those experiences.

Building a psychedelic library begins with an understanding of drug ideologies, followed by specific outlines for collecting and using psychedelic literature. Psychedelic substances from plant sources and some newer synthetic pharmaceuticals both will be covered in this review. Many substances deserve mention, but often, only secondary and tertiary literature can be listed, given the limitations of space. The development of an individual pharmacological repertoire is an ongoing, evolutionary, lifelong process. It is based on knowledge and reflection of psychedelic literature that is built in terms of a personal collection of works in the printed and other media.

The psychedelic literature consists of explorers who have studied the cultural origins of various substances, scientists who have researched the chemical and pharmacological aspects of molecules, and users who have recounted their experiences with psychedelic compounds. The growth of humankind's pharmacological knowledge is necessary, because it allows for the continued discovery of natural and synthetic psychedelic substances.

Ideologies of Drug Use

Most of the literature on psychedelic drugs is influenced strongly by the author's ideologies, or belief structures, about those drugs and their functions in a specific society. Different ideologies not only influence attitudes toward personal use or non-use and toward others' use, but they even can affect the very nature and meaning of the psychedelic experience.

In the scientific and medical fields, psychedelic drug experiences have been viewed in many negative ways, as initiators of mental illness and as tools to bring about model psychoses. Psychiatrists have used these substances with the idea of temporarily experiencing a state of psychiatric disorder, thus giving them a first-hand notion of their patient's reality. Psychedelics also have been viewed positively as aids in psychotherapy, meditative states, and other therapeutic contexts.

In a cross-cultural context, many psychedelic substances have been used traditionally in many societies and settings to enhance religious experiences, heal people, bond members of a social group, delineate societal hierarchies and conventions, and even create a sense of meaning and placement in this worldly existence.

In the 1950s and 1960s, psychedelic drugs became symbolic of a generation's attempts to address or attack social and moral issues. and the mass media soon employed LSD to stereotype particular subcultures with distinct attitudes and lifestyles. By the late 1960s and 1970s, the people also explored whether these substances may be doorways to global cooperation or to communication with other species and lifeforms. The 1980s and 1990s have brought a body of psychedelic literature that focuses on the wiring of the brain, biochemical explanations, and the achievement of transpersonal states of consciousness. The social and political contexts of each period is reflected in its literature.

Thus, several ideologies, perspectives, ethics, and functions for psychedelic drug use have evolved. The ways in which we view and use these substances are dependent upon the social context of the time. The powerful influence of drug use ideologies should be considered by everyone, users and non-users alike. In order to make wise and beneficial decisions about the use and non-use of psychedelic drugs, it is necessary to have access to information on their botanical, chemical, pharmacological, therapeutic, legal, behavioral, and social aspects.

Information scientists view literature as being primary, secondary, or tertiary in nature. Primary literature consists of original research reports and scholarly studies, first-hand accounts of drug experiences, and descriptions of innovative activities and programs. It usually is very technical or narrowly focused, and thus, it is meant for a specialized audience.

Secondary literature involves collecting, synthesizing, or reinterpreting the primary literature in order to make it more accessible and understandable to non-specialists, but it sacrifices some finer points and is open to the biases of the compiler or author. Tertiary literature is far removed from the original sources, and it is generated to further coalesce disparate aspects of a particular subject in simple and comprehendible terms, but at the loss of depth and important differences in the original information. In addition, some works consist simply of anthologies, or collections, of the primary literature on psychedelic drug use and experiences, and they can be valuable references.

Readers should be wary of embellishments, and they should try to discern the author's ideology or value foundation, as this can greatly influence what is and what is not reported and discussed. Comparisons to other written accounts and personal experiences always should be made, and similarities and differences noted for reflection and further study. The most useful works are those that are based on more than a single experience with a drug, though sometimes a single major experience might provide the structure for the narrative, such as Huxley's accounts of his mescaline experience. The best literature provides some insight, or at least chronicles, the fears, issues, and problems that can arise in studies of these substances.

Classic Literature and Working Texts

Early accounts and descriptions of specific cultural uses of psychedelic substances are valuable for providing historical perspective. Some of the best drug literature was developed around the turn of the century before the beginning of drug control legislation. Earlier studies and accounts usually were not hampered by the political, legal, moral, or social concerns and constraints that we have to deal with today.

Self-experimentation, in which the researcher serves as his or her own subject, has led traditionally to major drug discoveries. It allows for direct personal contact with the empirical world, for gathering useful scientific information, and for testing compounds that might become useful therapies for patients. Drug researchers have self-administered pharmacologically active compounds in order to assess short and long term effects, dose-response relationships, toxic reactions, and therapeutic applications. Accounts of self-experimentation can be very useful.

Research and cross-cultural information on some plant substances is limited, and consequently, potential mind explorers should exercise great caution. Information may exist regarding classical botanical or chemical studies or subcultural reports, but the depth and breadth of these experiences still may be very limited. Synthetic psychedelic compounds (now unfortunately referred to in the mainstream as "designer drugs") are a result of the pharmaceutical age. Basic principles of drug development have been applied to the search for new drugs with more specific effects. New substances are discovered regularly, often by people who are not directly connected with the traditional drug development process.

Personal and scientific accounts of the 19th century, often drawing on each other, provide the earliest well-documented studies of psychedelic drug experiments. Over the years a number of classic texts on the use of psychedelics have been written (see appendix, "Classic Working Texts"). These working texts, either articles or books, represent knowledge that users and potential users should review and consider in their studies of psychedelic drugs. These lists are meant to be modified and built upon with new additions and rediscovered works.

In recent years, a number of fine books have been published that review past efforts and call for a reconsideration of psychedelics. Their goal is the incorporation of these substances into our society and everyday lives under appropriate constraints but in more positive ways, so that safe and effective drug use can occur with minimal problems.

Psychedelic drugs have a number of beneficial applications. Past research has found uses in medicine and psychiatry, religion, literature, and the arts. Many people claim the right to explore and research areas that interest them and that promise benefits for their lives. Self-experimentation no longer is viewed only as a dramatic or romanticized scientific pursuit. Additional study of psychedelics always is warranted, not only to ascertain their beneficial effects, but also to determine the reasons for negative effects and untoward reactions so they can be minimized or eliminated.

A few guidebooks on growing and manufacturing psychedelics have been published by underground presses. Some of these books can provide valuable insight and information, but the complexities of the botanical and chemical techniques can be the source of many problems beyond the mere illegality of the activity. Those with adequate training and experience will have to turn to primary literature, while others may rely on secondary sources that can produce mixed results. A consideration of both the scientific and subcultural literature is necessary in order to use them well.[2]

Building a Library on Psychedelic Drugs

The classic literature is fundamental to an understanding of psychedelic substances.[3] It provides the working texts for further research and other inquiries. Additional references and other works can supplement this information (see appendix, "A Psychedelic Library"). The foundation for psychedelic knowledge is the building and maintaining of a personal library.

How does a drug researcher start and build a foundation for continued learning?

Once you have identified key references you wish to study, you are ready to begin purchasing books, magazines, and other printed materials, and by extension, audio, video and other media. The quickest way, short of purchasing an existing collection (someone's personal library), is to identify used, rare and antiquarian bookstores in your area or when you travel to other places.[4]

A regular perusal of specialized bookstores and book catalogues can be helpful, not only in purchasing books, but also in educating yourself about obscure, previously unknown works, and noting trends in the market value of such books. There also are a variety of academic, scholarly, popular, specialty, and subcultural journals and magazines, which contain articles and bibliographies on psychedelic drugs.[5] The bibliographies provided at the end of this essay may help you assess your current library and direct you to other working texts and useful references.

Applications and Meaning

The goal of psychedelic drug research should be the accumulation of knowledge and experience in a safe and rational manner. Problems resulting from use must be identified, so they can be minimized or prevented. Past research and cross-cultural examples have shown that drug use problems occur least often when drug taking takes place in a ceremonial or ritualized context with a cultural meaning. The application of formal and informal social controls in our society would enhance greatly the beneficial experiences that psychedelics can provide.

Havelock Ellis varied the dose, set, and setting of different peyote experiences to determine how the effects would change. He structured the setting, expectations, and reasons for use in an experimental manner. But it was not until the 1960s that user set and setting were recognized fully as major influences on the psychedelic experience. Controlling the set and setting of use has found great application, and is thoroughly described, in many self-experimentation and psychotherapeutic manuals, developed mostly in the 1960s.

As scientific research, therapeutic applications, and individual self-experimentation continue, the need to develop useful knowledge and appropriate reasons and methods for using psychedelics becomes more important. Users and non-users alike need to improve their awareness of the information that exists, its quality and accessibility, and the ways in which it is used to prevent or promote use. At the very least, identification and consideration of the literature on psychedelics can be helpful in limiting or preventing problems from their use. Far better, the exchange of information between scientists and subcultures can further our understanding and appreciation of the wonderful ongoing discoveries of these substances.

The time certainly has come for a full appreciation of the beneficial uses that psychedelic drugs have to offer. With renewed interest, it becomes necessary to understand better these chemical substances, their origins, effects, and dangers to guard against misuse and to allow for therapeutic and spiritual applications that are compatible with their uniquely characteristic actions. Let us join together in learning more about these drugs, and perhaps, we can realize and celebrate Albert Hofmann's dream that "if people would learn to use LSD's vision-inducing capability more wisely, under suitable conditions, in medical practice and in conjunction with meditation, then this problem child could become a wonder child."

Footnotes

1. These listings are meant to be representative and not comprehensive. There are other important and influential works that are not cited specifically herein. Bibliographies in many of the cited references, however, will direct you to other important texts.
2. Bibliographic information and reference lists are available through a number of information exchange services and associations, such as: Multidisciplinary Association for Psychedelic Studies (MAPS), Psychedelic Monographs and Essays (PM&E) Publishing Group, the Albert Hofmann Foundation, and Rosetta. A good place to begin with the academic literature is your local college library, especially medical libraries, and federally funded research is disseminated by the National Institute on Drug Abuse in Rockville, Maryland.
3. Literary and philosophical accounts of drug experiences have a long history and tradition. Such writings have been

important in describing certain types of experiences, directing the use of specific drugs, and even structuring an ideology of use that reflects a larger philosophy of life. The bibliographies in this article list these classics plus reports of investigations in psychotherapy, religion, creativity, exploration and expansion of consciousness, enhancement of communication, sensory awareness, alternate states of consciousness, physical and spiritual healing, and many other areas.

4. Look for booksellers who specialize in medicine and pharmacy (esp. psychiatry, pharmacology), social sciences (anthropology, sociology, psychology, history), natural sciences (botany), and criminal justice. Some booksellers have a section or shelf devoted to drugs, medicines, or related subjects. Many booksellers also will accept "want" lists, or they will note specific areas of interest to you and inform you of latest acquisitions. Some booksellers (medicine, science, technology, 1960s history) issue catalogues. One famous catalogue, *Phantastica: Rare and Important Psychoactive Drug Literature 1700 to the Present*, issued in 1979 by William and Victoria Dailey of Los Angeles still is used as a key guide to drug literature. Dealers often place ads in the magazines and other publications listed below. Some dealers and specific searching services will locate out-of-print and hard to find books. Recent and new publications are listed in *Books In Print* and other new book catalogues.

5. Important journals, magazines, and other regular publications include: *Journal of Ethnopharmacology, Harvard Botanical Museum Leaflets, Psychedelic Monographs and Essays, The Entheogen Review, Journal of Psychoactive Drugs, Journal of Drug Issues, International Journal of the Addictions, Drugs and Society,* and of course, *High Times.*

Classic Working Texts

Listed below are 22 classic working texts that should be a part of every psychedelic library. The majority of them, unfortunately, are no longer in print, and some of them can be difficult to find. Brackets show first edition dates.

Bernard Aaronson and Humphry Osmond (eds.). *Psychedelics: The Uses and Implications of Hallucinogenic Drugs.* Garden City, NY: Anchor Books, 1970.

This great collection of essays, edited by two pioneers in the field, focuses on the uses and roles of psychedelics in our society. The essays include: accounts of people's experiences, social and cultural perspectives, therapeutic applications and uses in schizophrenia, creativity, and religion. Some information is outdated, but principles remain very relevant, and it includes an extensive bibliography of the 1950s and 1960s literature.

Harold A. Abramson (ed.). *The Use of LSD in Psychotherapy and Alcoholism.* New York: Bobbs-Merrill, 1967.

The proceedings of the Second International Conference on the Use of LSD in Psychotherapy (1965) include contributions by the important psychedelic drug researchers of that time. It is a key 1960's source of information on therapeutic applications of LSD, and it provides many case studies and examples of growing impediments to research with these substances.

Russ Crescimanno. *Mind, Self and the Hallucinogens.* New York: MSS Information Corp., 1973.

This fascinating study of the collectivity of the psychedelic subculture, focusing on the search for meaningful experiences, provides an interesting theoretical framework (from the perspective of symbolic interactionism) for interpreting psychedelic drug effects and the ideology of the people involved. Results of interviews with college students in Connecticut and Virginia in the late 1960s and early 1970s provided for testing and refining the theory. In essence, the drug-induced state is viewed as highly variable and mostly ineffable, and symbols become a useful way for understanding the nature and meaning of such experiences.

R.A. Durr. *Poetic Vision and the Psychedelic Experience.* Syracuse, NY: Syracuse University Press, 1970.

This literary study describes the similarities between the worlds of psychedelic experiences and imaginative, visionary literature. Certain visionary, metaphysical, and philosophical elements recur in most psychedelic accounts and provide a view of the everyday world transfigured. Many well-known authors and their most important visionary works are cited, from Zen poets to 19th century romantics to the psychedelic writers of the 1960s.

Peter T. Furst. *Hallucinogens and Culture.* San Francisco: Chandler and Sharp, 1976.

Cross-cultural aspects of psychedelic drug use are explored by anthropologist Furst. This book, and his *Flesh of the Gods*, are among the best descriptions of how other cultures have utilized psychedelics with minimal problems, through ritual use in ceremonial contexts. The various major psychedelic substances are reviewed historically and cross-culturally, and the important roles they play in religion, healing, magic, and many other rituals are presented and discussed.

Lester Grinspoon and James B. Bakalar. *Psychedelic Drugs Reconsidered.* New York: Basic Books, 1979.

This reference text is the ultimate survey of psychedelic drugs, through its massive bibliography and its coverage of all aspects of use: botanical, chemical, pharmacological, literary, therapeutic, legal, and social. A good place to start with the identification of key works for a personal library on psychedelics, and a great overview of the subject matter in this field.

Stanislav Grof. *Realms of the Human Unconscious: Observations from LSD Research.* New York: E.P. Dutton, 1975.

From almost two decades of clinical research using psychedelic agents, Grof redefines our conception of the human unconscious. This is arguably the single most original work in the psychedelic literature. From many sessions with patients using LSD, he has examined perinatal and transpersonal experiences, the multidimensional nature of such experiences, and the systems of condensed experiences (a specific constellation of memories of experiences from different times in a person's life). His later works basically extend these ideas and offer further results from his extensive clinical research.

M.J. Harner (ed.) *Hallucinogens and Shamanism.* New York: Oxford University Press, 1973.

This collection of ten studies on the role of psychedelics in shamanism provides quite a range of examples historically and culturally. Many accounts include the investigator's perspective as participant in the various psychedelic experiences. There are wonderful descriptions of trance states, mystical experiences, and the cultural aspects of fascinating rituals and ceremonies, including Henry Munn's amazing portrait of shamanistic curing by the Mazatecs of Mexico using the "mushrooms of language."

Albert Hofmann. *LSD: My Problem Child.* J. Ott (trans.), Los Angeles: J.P. Tarcher, 1983.

The ultimate historical testament and fascinating reading, when it comes to the discovery of LSD, psilocybin, psilocin, and many other psychedelic compounds. The sense of adventure and exploration is evident as Albert pursues his dreams in search of therapeutically useful compounds from plants, only to create one of the most unique substances that science has ever synthesized.

Aldous Huxley. *The Doors of Perception*. New York: Harper, 1954.

One of the most influential accounts of psychedelic experience, and a lucid, exhilarating analysis of the metaphysics of mescaline. He focuses on the transformation of reality and the nature of a mystical experience that changed him forever.

Heinrich Kluver. *Mescal and Mechanisms of Hallucinations*. Chicago: University of Chicago Press, 1966 [1928].

This pioneering work on psychedelic visions has intrigued and inspired many succeeding drug researchers. Kluver equates many aspects of the psychedelic experience to delirious and psychotic states. A great complement to the works of Grof, Masters and Houston, and Moreau.

R.E.L. Masters and Jean Houston. *The Varieties of Psychedelic Experience*. New York: Holt, Rinehart and Winston, 1966.

Involved in many psychotherapeutic studies with psychedelic drugs, these two researchers describe their findings in scholarly and practical terms. This book, and their *Psychedelic Art*, reflect the spectrum of their activities. They basically attempt to apply William James' typology of religious experience to the psychedelic experience and its many facets.

Claudio Naranjo. *The Healing Journey: New Approaches to Consciousness*. New York: Pantheon, 1973.

An alternative look at the therapeutic value of psychedelic substances that focuses away from LSD to other compounds (MDA, MMDA, harmaline, and ibogaine). Using the technique of guided imagery, he explores the human unconscious, and he shows therapeutic advances through numerous case studies.

Jonathan Ott. *Hallucinogenic Plants of North America*. Berkeley: Wingbow Press, 1976.

A compendium of information on psychedelics from natural sources on this continent. All major plants are discussed, but the emphasis is on psychoactive mushrooms, the substances he has studied the most.

Walter Pahnke. *Drugs and Mysticism: An Analysis of the Relationship Between Psychedelic Drugs and the Mystical Experience*. Doctoral Dissertation, Cambridge: Harvard University Press, 1964.

The famous Good Friday psilocybin experiment at Marsh Chapel in 1962 forms the basis of Pahnke's dissertation. A very well-designed study, with a control group, that assessed the effects of psilocybin and more importantly, investigated the relationship between psychedelic experiences and religious or mystical states. While the dissertation is difficult to obtain, Pahnke reported much of it in other book chapters and articles in many anthologies list in the bibliography.

Gerardo Reichel-Dolmatoff. *The Shaman and the Jaguar: A Study of Narcotic Drugs Among the Indians of Colombia*. Philadelphia: Temple University Press, 1975.

To the people of the Northwest Amazon river basin, the shaman-into-jaguar transformation is central to their religious beliefs and experiences. This altered reality is entered with the assistance of narcotic snuffs, usually comprised of Benisteriopsis. The researcher also participated in the drug taking ceremony and his experience is woven into the results he presents and discusses.

Richard Evans Schultes and Albert Hofmann. *The Botany and Chemistry of Hallucinogens*. Second Edition. Springfield, IL: Charles C. Thomas, 1980 [1973].

The best comprehensive source on psychedelic substances from plants. As botanist and chemist, they evaluate and synthesize most of the available literature. Their personal experiences over five decades in the field, identifying, isolating, and creating specific compounds provide the perfect foundation, as well as an interesting historical perspective. Most of the book is written at a specialist level, and the terminology and methodology are complex. Most of the works cited come from the 1940-70s, but this book also provides anecdotal and cultural information.

Alexander Shulgin and Ann Shulgin. *PiHKAL: A Chemical Love Story.* Berkeley: Transform Press, 1991.

A truly amazing biographical account of a lifetime's work in psychedelic research. Sasha Shulgin is known for his work as a chemist synthesizing countless compounds in search of more therapeutically beneficial drugs. This massive work, co-written with his wife Ann, is divided into two sections: the first part focuses on the personal side of his work, and the second part provides extensive chemical information on 179 compounds.

Michael V. Smith. *Psychedelic Chemistry.* Second Edition. Port Townsend, WA: Loompanics, 1981 [1974].

An excellent guidebook to the chemical aspects of psychedelic substances. This is a very technical overview of the synthesis, analysis, and production of the major drugs, while additional, limited information is provided on many others.

Peter Stafford. *Psychedelics Encyclopedia.*Third Edition. Berkeley: Ronin Press, 1992 [1977].

Consider Stafford's book to be the general readers's guide to the psychedelic tradition, much like Schultes and Hofmann are the scholarly standard bearers. In fact, Stafford takes much of his information from Schultes and Hofmann and other key works. The latest edition is essentially a reprint of the second edition with a new section on MDMA and recent happenings in the world of psychedelia.

R. Gordon Wasson. *The Wondrous Mushroom: Mycolatry in Mesoamerica.* New York: McGraw-Hill, 1980.

A great deal of confusion surrounded psychoactive fungi and the existence of mushroom cults, until Gordon Wasson's discoveries of the 1950s and 1960s, which are encapsulated in this book. This work, by one of the great "amateur" adventurer-scientists, reviews his work identifying the mushrooms and describing their effects and ritual uses. These mushroom cults unfortunately have been altered or destroyed by western influences, and their practices have been misreported by many outsiders. Little of their valuable ritualized pattern of use has carried over to users in contemporary society.

Norman Zinberg. *Drug, Set, and Setting.* New Haven, CT: Yale University Press, 1984.

Psychedelic drugs are not the major focus of this work, but its ideas and methods have profound implications for their beneficial use. Zinberg has been a strong advocate for the importance of set and setting in drug taking. Much of his work, along with the cross-cultural studies, have shown that purposeful and socially integrated drug use produces leads to more positive experience, while unstructured and poorly reasoned drug use produces more problems. Formal and informal social control mechanisms also are valuable in preventing or limiting the occurrence of drug use problems.

A Psychedelic Library

David F. Aberle. *The Peyote Religion Among the Navaho.* Chicago: Aldine, 1966.

Sophia Adamson (ed.). *Through the Gateway of the Heart: Accounts of Experiences with MDMA and Other Empathogenic Substances.* San Francisco: Four Trees, 1985.

Patrick Allain. *Hallucinogens et Societe.* Paris: Payot, 1973.

Lawrence K. Altman. *Who Goes First? The Story of Self-Experimentation in Medicine.* New York: Random House, 1987.

Edward F. Anderson. *Peyote: The Divine Cactus.* Tucson AZ: University of Arizona Press, 1980.

Antonin Artaud. *The Peyote Dance.* H. Weaver (trans.). New York: Farrar, Straus and Giroux, 1976 [1948].

Theodore X. Barber. *LSD, Marijuana, Hypnosis & Yoga.* Chicago: Aldine, 1970.

Harriet L. Barr and Robert J. Langs. *LSD: Personality and Experience.* New York: John Wiley and Sons, 1972.

Charles Baudelaire. *Artificial Paradise: On Hashish and Wine as Means of Expanding Individuality.* E. Fox (trans.). London: Herder and Herder, 1971 [1860].

Fernando Benitez. *In the Magic Land of Peyote.* J. Upton (trans.). Austin: University of Texas Press, 1975.

Lisa Bieberman. *Session Games People Play: A Manual for the Use of LSD.* Cambridge, MA: Psychedelic Information Center, 1967.

Malden G. Bishop. *The Discovery of Love: A Psychedelic Experience with LSD 25.* New York: Dodd, Mead and Co., 1963.

Richard H. Blum (ed.). *Utopiates: The Use and Users of LSD-25.* New York: Atherton, 1964.

William Braden. *The Private Sea: LSD and the Search for God.* Chicago: Quadrangle, 1967.

William Burroughs and Allen Ginsberg. *The Yage Letters.* San Francisco: City Lights Books, 1963.

Frank J. Bove. *The Story of Ergot.* Basel: S. Karger, 1970.

Roberto Cavanna and Emilio Servadio. *ESP Experiments with LSD-25 and Psilocybin.* New York: Parapsychology Foundation, 1964.

Louis Cholden (ed.). *Lysergic Acid Diethylamide and Mescaline in Experimental Psychiatry.* New York: Grune and Stratton, 1956.

Walter Houston Clark. *Chemical Ecstasy: Psychedelic Drugs and Religion.* New York: Sheed and Ward, 1969.

Sidney Cohen. *The Beyond Within.* New York: Atheneum, 1964.

Barnaby Conrad. *Absinthe: A History in a Bottle.* San Francisco: Chronicle Books, 1988.

Bernard Copley. *Hallucinogenic Drugs and Their Application to Extrasensory Perception.* Joshua Tree, CA: Hypnosophic Inst., 1962.

Richard Crocket, R.A. Sandison and A. Walk (eds.). *Hallucinogenic Drugs and Their Psychotherapeutic Use.* London: H.K. Lewis, 1963.

E. Wade Davis. *Passage of Darkness: The Ethnobiology of the Haitian Zombie*. Chapel Hill, NC: University of North Carolina Press, 1988.

Richard C. DeBold and Russel C. Leaf (eds.). *LSD, Man and Society*. Middletown, CT: Wesleyan University Press, 1967.

Richard De Mille (ed.). *The Don Juan Papers: Further Castaneda Controversies*. Santa Barbara, CA: Ross-Erikson, 1980 [1976].

Marlene Dobkin de Rios. *Visonary Vine: Hallucinogenic Healing in the Peruvian Amazon*. Prospect Heights, IL: Waveland Press, 1984 [1972].

Marlene Dobkin de Rios. *Hallucinogens: Cross-Cultural Perspectives*. Albuquerque: University of New Mexico Press, 1984.

Jane Dunlop (pseud: Adele Davis). *Exploring Inner Space: Personal Experiences Under LSD-25*. New York: Harcourt Brace Jovanovich, 1961.

Brian Du Toit (ed.). *Drugs, Rituals and Altered States of Consciousness*. Rotterdam: A.A. Balkema, 1977.

Daniel H. Efron (ed.). *Psychotomimetic Drugs*. New York: Raven Press, 1970.

Bruce Eisner. *Ecstasy: The MDMA Story*. Berkeley: Ronin, 1989.

Havelock Ellis. "Mescal, A Study of a Divine Plant." *Popular Science Monthly* 61:52-71, May 1902.

Alvaro Estrada. *Maria Sabina: Her Life and Chants*. H. Munn (trans.). Santa Barbara: Ross-Erikson, 1981.

Peter T. Furst (ed.). *Flesh of the Gods: The Ritual Use of Hallucinogens.* New York: Praeger, 1972.

James R. Gamage and Edmund L. Zerkin (eds). *Hallucinogenic Drug Research: Impact on Science and Society.* Beloit, WI: Stash Press, 1970.

Gracie and Zarkov. *Notes From Underground, Volume 1.* Preliminary Edition, n.p.: Gracie and Zarkov Productions, 1985.

Lester Grinspoon and James Bakalar (ed.). *Psychedelic Reflections.* New York: Human Science Press, 1983.

Stanislav Grof. *LSD Psychotherapy.* Pomona, CA: Hunter House, 1980.

Stanislav Grof and Joan Halifax. *The Human Encounter With Death.* New York: E.P. Dutton, 1977.

Hudson Grubber. *Growing the Hallucinogens.* Berkeley, CA: Level Press, 1973.

S.I Hayakawa (ed.). Special Issue on the Psychedelic Experience. *ETC: Review of General Semantics* 22:389-528, December 1965.

Alethea Hayter. *Opium and the Romantic Imagination.* Berkeley: University of California Press, 1968.

Roger Heim. *Les Champignons Toxiques et Hallucinogenes.* Paris: Societe Nouvelle des Editions Boubee, 1978.

Roger Heim and R. Gordon Wasson. *Les Champignons*

Hallucinogenes due Mexique. Paris: Edition Museum National d'Histoire Naturelle, 1958.

Abram Hoffer and Humphrey Osmond. *The Hallucinogens.* New York: Academic Press, 1967.

Aldous Huxley. Moksha: *Writings on Psychedelics and the Visionary Experience.* M. Horowitz and C. Palmer (eds.), Los Angeles: J.P. Tarcher, 1977.

B.L. Jacobs (ed.). *Hallucinogens: Neurochemical, Behavioral and Clinical Perspectives.* New York: Raven Press, 1984.

V. Joyson. *The Acid Trip: A Complete Guide to Psychedelic Music.* Todmorden, UK: Babylon Books, 1984.

Art Kleps. *Millbrook: The True Story of the Early Years of the Psychedelic Revolution.* Oakland: Bench Press, 1977.

Weston LaBarre. *The Peyote Cult.* Enlarged Edition. New York: Schocken Books, 1969 [1938].

Timothy Leary. *Flashbacks: An Autobiography.* Los Angeles: J.P. Tarcher, 1983.

Timothy Leary, Ralph Metzner and Richard Alpert. *The Psychedelic Experience: A Manual Based on the Tibetan Book of the Dead.* Secaucus, NJ: Citadel Press, 1964.

Martin A. Lee and Bruce Shlain. *Acid Dreams.* New York: Grove Press, 1985.

John Lilly. *The Scientist.* New York: Bantam Books, 1981.

John Uri Lloyd. *Etidorhpa.* Eleventh Edition. Caldwell, ID: Caxton Press, 1901 [1895].

Bernard Lowy and Michael Montagne. *Psychoactive Fungi of the World*. New Haven, CT: Yale University Press, 1993.

Luis Eduardo Luna and Pablo Amaringo. *Ayahuasca Visions: The Religious Iconograpy of a Peruvian Shaman*. Berkeley: North Atlantic Books, 1991.

R.E.L. Masters and Jean Houston. *Psychedelic Art*. New York: Grove Press, 1968.

David P. McAllester. *Peyote Music*. New York: Viking Fund, 1949.

Terence McKenna. *Food of the Gods*. New York: Basic Books, 1992.

Ralph Metzner (ed.). *The Ecstatic Adventure*. New York: MacMillan, 1968.

Roger E. Meyer (ed.). *Adverse Reactions to Hallucinogenic Drugs*. Washington: U.S. Government Printing Office, 1969.

Henri Michaux. *Miserable Miracle (Mescaline)*. New York: Orion Press, 1963 [1956].

Henri Michaux. *Infinite Turbulence*. London: Calder and Boyars, 1975 [1964].

Michael Montagne. "Pharmacology and Probability." *The Psychozoic Press* No. 6, pp. 61-66, Winter 1983.

Michael Montagne. "The Metaphorical Nature of Drugs and Drug Taking." *Social Science and Medicine* 26:417-24, 1988.

Michael Montagne (ed.). "Philosophies of Drug Giving and Drug Taking." *Journal of Drug Issues* 18:139-284, Spring 1988.

Michael Montagne. "From Problem Child to Wonder Child: LSD Turns 50." *M.A.P.S. Newsletter* Vol. 4, No. 1, Spring 1993.

Michael Montagne and Donald D. Vogt. "Toward an Integrative Framework for the Comprehensive Study of Drug-Taking Behaviors and Experiences." *International Journal of Addictions* 18:959-70, 1983.

Jacques-Joseph Moreau. *Hashish and Mental Illness.* G.J. Barnett (trans.). New York: Raven Press, 1973 [1845].

Barbara G. Myerhoff. *Peyote Hunt: The Sacred Journey of the Huichol Indians.* Ithaca, NY: Cornell University Press, 1974.

Constance A. Newland. *My Self and I.* New York: New American Library, 1962.

Daniel C. Noel (ed.). *Seeing Castaneda.* New York: Perigee Books, 1976.

Jonathan Ott and Jeremy Bigwood (eds.). *Teonanacatl: Hallucinogenic Mushrooms of North America.* Seattle: Madrona Publ., 1978.

Vincenzo Petrullo. *The Diabolic Root. A Study of Peyotism, the New Indian Religion, Among the Delawares.* New York: Farrar, Straus and Giroux, 1975.

S. Radouco-Thomas, A. Villenueve and C. Radouco-Thomas (eds.). *Pharmacology, Toxicology and Abuse of Psychoto-*

mimetics (Hallucinogens). Quebec: Les Presses de l'Universite Laval, 1974.

Christian Ratsch (ed.). *Gateway to Inner Space: Sacred Plants, Mysticism and Psychotherapy.* Bridport, Dorset, UK: Prism, 1989.

Thomas J. Riedlinger (ed.). *The Sacred Mushroom-Seeker: Essays for R. Gordon Wasson.* Portland, OR: Dioscorides, 1990.
Bernard Roseman. *LSD—The Age of Mind.* Hollywood: Wilshire, 1963.

D.V. Siva Sankar (ed.). *LSD: A Total Study.* Westbury, NY: PJD Publ., 1975.

Hedwig Schleiffer. *Sacred Narcotic Plants of the New World Indians: An Anthology of Texts from the 16th Century to Date.* New York: Harper Press, 1973.

Hedwig Schleiffer. *Narcotic Plants of the Old World: An Anthology of Texts from Ancient Times to the Present.* Monticello, NY: Lubrecht and Cramer, 1979.

Richard Evans Schultes. *Hallucinogenic Plants.* New York: Golden Guide, 1976.

Richard Evans Schultes and Albert Hofmann. *Plants of the Gods.* New York: McGraw-Hill, 1979.

Richard Evans Schultes and Robert F. Raffauf. *The Vine of the Soul.* Tucson, AZ: Synergetics, 1992.

Alexander T. Shulgin. *Controlled Substances.* Revised Edition. Berkeley: Ronin, 1991.

Ronald K. Siegel and L.J. West (eds.). *Hallucinations: Behavior, Experience and Theory.* New York: John Wiley and Sons, 1975.

David Solomon (ed.). *LSD: The Consciousness-Expanding Drug.* New York: G.P. Putnam's, 1964.

Peter Stafford. *Psychedelic Baby Reaches Puberty.* New York: Praeger, 1971.

Peter G. Stafford and Bonnie H. Golightly. *LSD: The Problem-Solving Psychedelic.* New York: Award Books, 1967.

Jay Stevens. *Storming Heaven: LSD and the American Dream.* New York: Atlantic Monthly Press, 1987.

Omer C. Stewart. *Washo-Northern Paiute Peyotism: A Study in Acculturation.* Berkeley: University of California Press, 1944.

R.C. Stillman and R.E. Willette (eds.). *The Pharmacology of the Hallucinogens.* New York: Pergamon Press, 1978.

Charles C. Tart (ed.). *Altered States of Consciousness.* New York: John Wiley and Sons, 1969.

J. Thomas Ungerleider (ed.). *The Problems and Prospects of LSD.* Springfield, IL: Charles C. Thomas, 1968.

Anthony F.C. Wallace. "Cultural Determinants of Response to Hallucinatory Experience." *Archives General Psychiatry.* 1:58-69, 1959.

R. Gordon Wasson. *Soma: Divine Mushroom of Immortality.* The Hague: Mouton, 1968.

R. Gordon Wasson, Albert Hofmann, and Carl A.P. Ruck. *The Road to Eleusis: Unveiling the Secret of the Mysteries.* New York: Harcourt Brace Jovanovich, 1978.

Alan W. Watts. *The Joyous Cosmology.* New York: Vintage, 1962.

W. David Watts. *The Psychedelic Experience: A Sociological Study.* Beverly Hills: Sage, 1971.

Andrew Weil. *The Marriage of the Sun and the Moon.* Boston: Houghton-Mifflin, 1980.

Andrew Weil. *The Natural Mind.* Revised Edition. Boston: Houghton Mifflin, 1986 [1972].

Gunther M. Weil, Ralph Metzner and Timothy Leary (eds.). *The Psychedelic Reader.* Secaucus, NJ: Citadel Press, 1973 [1965].

Brian Wells. *Psychedelic Drugs.* New York: Jason Aronson, 1974.

John White (ed.). *The Highest State of Consciousness.* Garden City, NY: Anchor, 1972.

Johannes Wilbert. *Tobacco and Shamanism in South America.* New Haven, CT: Yale University Press, 1987.